Praise for

Fiona's intimate account of a man's life is a powerful work of the ... courageous, tender, exasperated, angry, lyrical and occasionally even funny, but never voyeuristic. The simplicity of the prose and the honesty of observation are compelling.

Blake Morrison

Powerful and precise writing. It tackles elusive emotional states in a highly nuanced way. The detail is so lovingly preserved and presented.

Sasha Dugdale

Rarely have I felt so transported by someone else's words. Fiona draws you into the most intimate and personal of spaces and offers you the privilege of sharing thirty-six hours that would normally be invisible to the outside world. With great honesty and generosity, she invites us into her home as she cares for her dying husband. It's an invitation you won't want to turn down.

Bobbie Farsides, Professor of Clinical and Biomedical Ethics, Brighton and Sussex Medical School

36 Hours addresses an area of real current debate and interest and does so in a way that prioritises both aesthetic and human concerns equally. Committed and talented writing.

Chris Gribble, National Centre for Writing

The writing is vivid and very clear, highlighting the delicate balance and poignancy of the work involved in end-of-life care and the minutiae of support involved in the simplest of daily activities, making the mundane poetic. A remarkable piece of work.

Kate Flatt OBE

Deeply moving and intensely raw.

Li Mills

I'm in awe of the honesty and openness with which Fiona described her experience. Her account is a wonderful way of opening up some much-needed conversations about death and dying, not only at a public/societal level but, also at the patient-professional level.

Dr Simone Ali, Consultant in Palliative Medicine

36 Hours

Fiona Mason

Word after Word

Published by Word After Word Press 2022

FE20221

Word After Word Press
PO Box 13285
Colchester
CO7 9YY

www.wordafterword.org.uk

ISBN 978-1-9161655-2-6

A CIP catalogue record for this book is available from the
British Library.

Cover illustration © Fiona Mason 2022
Design and layout by Sara Holloway, www.saraholloway.com
Printed and bound in Great Britain by Clays Ltd, Elcograf S.p.A.

For M

Do not go gentle into that good night.
Rage, rage against the dying of the light.

— *Dylan Thomas*

Months shrink to days, hours
the secret, silken line pulls:
dandelion clocks.

6 am

Last night, after the three hours it took to get to the toilet and back, to change the bed, to negotiate the medication, he told me I'm very irritating.

It was after a day of navigating and cajoling, of tending to every need and making up for, of being tender and not losing my patience. And the weeks of trying to get him to eat something, anything.

After eleven months of helping through the tests, procedures, bad news, chemotherapy, radiotherapy, the incremental decline. All the awful glimmers of hope, which I've held carefully as a newborn, for both of us. After enabling his wish to die at home.

I'm irritating. Really, very irritating.

What I know is that I'm exhausted and tired of putting on a brave nurse-y face. I want things back the way they were, in the time before all of this. Late-night conversations over wine and passion and laughs and plans. I want all the ordinary irritations and tender squabbles of fourteen years under the same roof.

Lying awake since 5 am, I've been observing this murmuration of words move through my mind, break apart and reform into different configurations. Nothing changes, but nothing stays the same. My husband is no longer who he was. He is being consumed by himself and soon he'll be gone. And I don't know whether his jibes are because of the morphine or the secondary tumours that have seeded in his brain or a now permanent state of being so pissed-off about what's going on that he's just acting plain mean. He's dying, at home, and I guess we're both doing our best, under the circumstances.

My bubble of solitude is burst by the sound of Margaret's sensible shoes soft-stepping up the open wooden staircase. She's the second Marie Curie night nurse to stay over, her presence meant to give me a brief respite and a night in my own bed.

She brings me a mug of tea and leaves me to surface in my own time. I cup the hot china hard against my palms and sip at the almost scalding drink. The pain is so immediate and irrefutable that it cuts through the self-reflection that can easily slide into dark melancholy, which I don't have time for.

By the time I pad downstairs in my slippers and fleecy dressing gown, grey light is seeping through the curtains into the living room. Margaret comes through from the kitchen and tells me that Michael's been quiet all night and that she'll be on her way.

I follow her down the hallway, closing the front door behind her, trying to be as quiet as I can, conscious of the neighbours at the early hour. I wince as she slams her car door shut, revs the engine, and then kangaroos up the road and back into the world. The ensuing silence is tangible.

Pushing open the door to the front room, until recently our spare room for guests, I'm confronted by the sight of the hospital bed. I can't get used to it. Every morning it's as if I'm seeing it for the first time.

Michael is fast asleep. The duvet and blanket barely rise and fall. The pneumatic mattress huffs and puffs. For a while, all I can do is stand motionless and watch him doing nothing.

One of our cats wanders in, looks up at me and meows. 'No change then?' I imagine her saying.

'No. Are you hungry, Polly?'

She meows a yes, and turns and walks out of the room, tail in the air.

'I'll just go and feed the cats, then,' I say to Michael.

Michael says nothing. We have more and more conversations like this.

7 am

I make the effort to maintain a personal routine. My daily ablutions are almost religious in their ritual and help me keep things on track.

The shower cubicle feels private, almost confessional. I relish the hot needles landing on my head, the roaring water drowning out the closed silence in the house that's otherwise only rippled by the breathing bed beating time. I want to disappear, to wash myself away, to dissolve everything that life has become.

I ruminate over whether the water-processing plant removes the residues of sadness that must now be swirling down the plughole, or if it remains in the water in minute dilutions, like homoeopathy. If it does, I guess we're all drinking these distillations of people's lives and absorbing them into our own, every time we fill the kettle and make a brew, unless of course boiling the water eradicates such sediments.

I also wonder if every day is going to be like this from now on, because every day has been like this for a while now. I seem to have aged outside of my previous idea of time and become someone I don't entirely recognise.

I turn off the water, step out of the steam into the cold of the shower room and wipe condensation from the mirror with my towel, leaving little flecks of white fluff on the glass. I'm getting thinner and the corners of my mouth hang in a habitual downturn. My ears ring with constant blue-white tinnitus. I shake my head to clear the racket, but without effect, get busy drying myself and try to shift my focus towards what must happen today.

The district nurse will arrive soon, and the personal care woman. And then the kids are visiting.

It's 7.15 am when the beeping starts.

Beep –. Beep –. Beep –.

Alerting us to the fact that the syringe in the driver is empty.

Beep –. Beep –. Beep –.

A little under two weeks ago, I placed the syringe driver in our clothes peg bag, emptied and recommissioned for the purpose, and hung it on the head of the hospital bed.

Beep –. Beep –. Beep –.

It doesn't wake Michael. Not at first. He's in a distant, deep sleep.

Beep –. Beep –. Beep –.

The incessant noise is now a straight line of sound drawn with a fine-pointed mapping pen, starting in the middle of my forehead and ending at the base of my skull.

Beep –. Beep –. Beep –.

I can't turn it off, because the district nurse has locked the clear plastic box encasing the syringe driver and only she can undo it. When the noise pierces into Michael's consciousness, he stirs and looks around the room through half-lidded eyes, searching for the source of the sound.

Beep –. Beep –. Beep –.

He no longer puts two and two together and looks bewildered.

'Morning, my lovely,' I say. He tries to reply, but in his dry mouth, words ball into a mumble.

Beep –. Beep –. Beep –.

After fourteen minutes of this, I wonder if I can get a hammer from the garage, smash open the damned driver box and SHUT IT THE FUCK UP!

And breathe...

At fifteen minutes, we're saved by the arrival of the district nurse, by which time I've numbed myself to the piercing sound, as though breaking through an inner barrier and reaching a state of Zen transcendence. This one is Beverley. She's got spiky blonde hair, cheerful, soft round cheeks and still, grey eyes that don't fit her personality. I greet her with a smile, something I do with all the nurses, regardless of how I'm feeling.

She walks into the house and marches straight down the hall, as if she lives here, calling out, 'Morning, Michael, how are we today?'

He manages a feeble 'Hello, nurse.'

'Let's get you sorted, shall we?' she says.

'Yes please,' he says, this time with a bit more emphasis but still tentative, like he's either very young or very old and has been practising but is still getting the hang of speech.

At last, Beverley unlocks the syringe driver and shuts it off.

The silence comes as a surprise and a blessed emptiness is restored inside my head for me to re-inhabit. So that's where a fragment of me goes, to find a dark inner corner where I can curl up and suck my thumb and twirl a lock of hair and pretend none of this is happening.

Beverley unthreads the syringe driver box through Michael's clothing, following the clear plastic line to the blue butterfly needle that's inserted into his wasted forearm, providing a running commentary as she goes, 'There we are then, oops-a-daisy, here we go, nearly there, let's have this old thing out and pop in a nice fresh one.'

Michael responds with a warm, grateful smile and a cheeky eye, something he seems to reserve for nurses. Out of nowhere, I am swallowed up by hot jealousy.

She's not irritating, oh no. He's got time for her. Lovely, smiley, warm Beverley. I loathe myself for this idiotic resentment, because I don't for a moment believe that in his hospital bed, at the end stages of cancer, he's got designs on her. I know it's irrational and I know it's because I'm exhausted and because despite my apparent resilience, this situation is completely, relentlessly unbearable. I crave every drop of affection, kind words, warm smiles, and gratitude that my husband has to bestow. Quite simply, right now, I don't want to share.

Of course, their easy manner is precisely because their roles are bounded, prescribed and transactional: he's the patient, she's the nurse. Their communication isn't loaded with the panic of having to say everything before it's too late. I leave Beverley to her nursing and go and make her a coffee: white and two sugars. When I return with her drink, it's to the living room, where she's decamped to sit at our dining table, the table Michael and I chose together and put just there, in that spot beside the open wooden staircase.

I have given the nurses a seagrass basket in

which to keep their supplies. It's the one we used to use in the bathroom for soaps and shower gels, bath bombs and scented candles.

Now it contains enemas, syringes, needles, dressings, wipes, pads, surgical gloves, and a great stock of medication. Next to that is the yellow box for sharps that says Danger! Biohazard. And next to that, a turned wooden bowl half-filled with apples that have started to wrinkle and smell as fusty as autumn windfalls.

The nurse's ritual is the same each morning. First, open the blue folder and find the sheet relating to the administering of controlled substances. Then check the number from yesterday and count the phials of morphine to make sure that none have gone missing in the night. Once she's checked everything, disassemble the syringe driver and remove the large syringe: 18mm in diameter, and 60mm long. Disassemble the syringe. Check off the reading from the digital display. Take out a new syringe. Take out a new needle. Check the prescription. Fit the needle to the syringe. Gather the morning medications. 20mg of diamorphine for pain, and 12mg of metoclopramide for nausea. Push the needle into each phial and draw in the liquid. Check the level on the side of the syringe. Write it down. Remove the needle from the syringe and attach the line. Fit the syringe back into the driver. Enter the volume of medication and rate of release into the digital display. Close the box. Lock it down. All done.

I've watched the ritual so many times that I have been picturing all of this while sitting on Michael's huffing-puffing hospital bed. Things happen so slowly these days. First, wake up. Second, the district nurse and syringe driver. Third? Well, that will be after she's gone. Worry about it then.

'The kids are coming today,' I say.

'Are they?' says Michael. His voice is small and feeble.

I've brought him a mug half-filled with tea, which he struggles to hold and barely drinks. I'm not sure what he wants anymore, if anything at all, but I long for this ritual of the ordinary: first tea of the day with sugar, and a cigarette. Although I quit six years ago, and Michael hasn't had a smoke since last April when the doctor called to say there was a shadow on his lung.

'Have you had enough?' I ask, and he nods.

For the last week and a half, he's been less interested in drinking, but there's no forcing it. Just a regular offer of water or tea or juice. His hands have developed the involuntary twitch of a much older man. I ease the mug from his grasp and put it on the bookcase.

Michael starts picking at my mauve cardigan, at the little purple and pink beads that edge the hook-and-eye fastening, and then at the knitted fabric. 'The thread,' he says. 'It's the thread, here.' He is picking at the air. 'Hold this one,' he says. 'You've got to hold it because I've got to get this one.' He opens my palm and with great care, he puts nothing into it and squeezes my fingers into a fist. 'You hold that. I've got to get these ones,' he says, his fingers picking at what is invisible to me, things in front of his eyes.

At 7.45 am, Beverley comes in to refit the syringe driver. 'Nearly done Michael,' she sings.

'Don't let go!' says Michael, fixing me in his gaze. I close my fingers tight.

'Don't worry, I won't.' I get off the bed to give Beverley some space.

Michael's skin has become paper-thin, and it takes her a while and several attempts to find somewhere to insert the butterfly needle. She opts for the left side of his chest. The needle's a good inch and a half long. It doesn't bother him, but I can see the steel profile under the surface of his skin, and it bothers me he's so indifferent to it.

Needle in, clear adhesive pad in place, she drops the syringe driver into the repurposed clothes-peg bag and hangs it back onto the bedstead. The old woven bag in faded reds, pinks and oranges is one I bought two decades before in Oxfam, and I never imagined it being used for its current purpose. Until a couple of weeks ago, I'd never heard of syringe drivers. Now I understand it's just one entry amongst others in the occult lexicon of terminal illness.

'There we are, my love, all done,' says Beverley.

I stand at the front door, watching her march down the road towards her car. She has plump thighs that rub together as she walks. Her fuchsia pink anorak is stretched tightly across her backside. She moves with purpose, talking into her mobile, connecting with the world. I gently push the door shut. We're left to ourselves, and the silence is a bandage wrapped rather too tightly around the house.

———

8 am

'Okay love, shall we get along to the loo?'

'Yes please,' says Michael.

I find the controller and push the button to raise the bed and then press another button to angle it until he is sitting upright. Then I move the covers and help Michael lift one foot and then the other and then to swivel around until his legs are over the side and his feet are on the floor. It's exhausting, so we have a rest.

'What's this?' says Michael, pulling at the plastic line of the driver.

'It's the line of your syringe driver.'

He looks at me and back at the line. 'And what's this?' he says, still pulling at the plastic line.

'It's the tube that goes to your syringe driver.'

He looks at me and looks back at the line. Time passes, Michael repeating the question over and over until I run out of ways to say the same thing without sounding patronising. 'But what's this one?' he says, pulling at the line that's now looped on his lap.

'It's your syringe driver line.' I say.

He looks at me, into me, almost, and then back at the line. 'This?' he says, now feeling where the line goes into the bag that is hanging on the side of the bed.

'It's the line that goes from you to your syringe driver.'

He looks at me as if I am speaking utter nonsense and then looks back at the line. He becomes distracted and looks at the bookshelf. 'What's that?' he says. 'That blue one. What's that?'

'It's Rick Stein's *Taste of the Sea*,' I say.

He looks at me and then back at the line. 'Sea? But what's this?' he says, pulling again at the plastic line.

'It's the line from your syringe driver.'

'Is it to have a piss with?'

'No, no, love, it's part of your syringe driver!'

His eyes say *I don't believe you*, but I also sense something else there, something wilful, mischievous, even a little bit cruel. I feel like I'm being toyed with, the way cats get long play out of a caught mouse. He never does this kind of verbal play with the kids or with the nurses. Just with me. For an instant, I doubt his motives and my doubt shames me.

Then he looks back at the line. 'What's this?' he says, pulling at the plastic line, harder this time.

'Please Michael, it's the line of your syringe driver. You mustn't pull it!'

'Syringe driver?' he says.'

'Yes, syringe driver,' I say.

An hour passes like this, long enough to turn my doubt and shame around, to find something to be grateful for, and it is this: that whatever his self has become, he can be it with me absolute. Most of all, it's almost all there is now, so, despite the frustration, I don't really want it to stop.

9 am

When it finally does stop, I fetch the walking sticks. One is plain wood. The other is my Alpenstock, the alpine walking stick with the little metal badges hammered along its shaft and a cork pressed over the metal spike at the end, for safety.

My mum bought me the stick in Austria on our first family holiday abroad. I started my periods that holiday. I was thirteen. There's a badge to mark all the experiences we had on that trip, but no badge to mark me starting my periods. They don't do badges for that sort of thing, and no one talked about it. Just like we don't talk about dying. Not with each other. Not with anyone.

'Hold on to the sticks, I'm just going to raise

the bed higher,' I say, and he hangs on as the hydraulics kick in and the bed unfolds him.

As it rises, I ease my shoulder under an arm and put a hand on his back and give a little push as he leans forward onto the sticks. And we're up. I place my hands on either side of his waist while he leans into the sticks and we begin the slow walk down the hallway to the shower room; me supporting and guiding and steering, him teetering like a novice on stilts.

The syringe driver bag is hanging around Michael's neck. We stop several times to have a look at the line and determine what it is and what it isn't. We take a quarter of an hour to walk five yards. When we reach our destination, it is 9.30 am.

Last week, the equipment loan people delivered a frame to go around the toilet, so there is something to hold on to when getting on and off. I help Michael with his pyjamas and onto the loo and then leave him in peace while I go and make the bed.

The mattress is a horrible plastic thing that doesn't smell like it should be in our home. The sheets don't stay put. They slide about, creating ridges and rucks. I get the bed straight, plump pillows and shake down the duvet.

All is silent down the hallway. I go to the kitchen for fresh water and a small bowl of chilled pineapple from the fridge and then put these on the bedside table. I open the curtains, raise the bamboo blind and open the windows to air the room. Then I think better of it and quickly close the windows and lower the blind. Our house is on the bend of the road, so the front window looks straight down it. With the blind open, Michael in his hospital bed would be in full view of every car and every passer-by, which naturally he wouldn't like. Especially given that no one is to know that he is ill.

I walk down the hall and call to Michael, 'Are you finished?'

'Yes,' he says.

I push open the shower room door. He is sitting where I left him, holding the plastic line in his hands.

'I've been trying to go, but I can't make it work,' he says, holding up the line to show me.

'That line is nothing to do with going to the loo,'

I say. 'It's the line of your syringe driver.'

He looks at me and back at the line. 'What's this?' he says, pulling at it.

'It's the line of your syringe driver.' I say.

'But I can't make it work!' he says.

'You don't have to,' I say. 'It works by itself.'

He looks at me and back at the line. 'But what is it?' he says, getting more emphatic and more distressed by his own confusion.

'It's nothing,' I say, 'nothing to worry about. Let's get you sorted; you're getting cold.'

He looks at me and back at the line. 'But I can't make it work!' he shouts, pulling at the plastic line.

'It's the line of your syringe driver.' I say. 'You don't have to do anything. You really mustn't pull on it.'

It is nearing 10 am by the time we get back to the front room. Michael's tiredness is profound. He loosens the grip on one stick and puts an arm around my neck, leaning into me. Then, like a kinetic sculpture, we move towards the bed as one, me, him and stick. It's not graceful.

'I don't feel well,' he says.

'It's the effort. Breathe steadily. Take your time.'

'I feel weird,' he says. 'I don't feel well.' And with that, his legs give way, and he crumples to the floor, pulling me with him.

We huddle there for some time, heaped and mingled like a pile of discarded clothes between the bed and the bookcase.

'Just rest here a moment,' I say. 'There's no rush. We've got all the time in the world.' Words I regret as soon as they fall off my tongue.

'I really feel ill,' something he never says despite being so ill. 'Aren't you going to call someone?'

'Let's try to get you up into bed,' I say. He is tall, and a dead weight pitted against my short, slight frame. 'Try getting up onto your knees first.'

It takes everything he has and several attempts to get onto all fours, each time slumping back onto his heels, breathless, until finally, he manages it. From there I stand behind him and then squat forward, putting my arms around and under his chest, trying not to catch the site of the butterfly needle. With a shared force of effort and will, I heave him onto the lowered bed where we both sit slumped in silence.

This hasn't happened before. The legs giving

way is a new thing that we must process. I leave Michael sitting on the bed, fetch the phone and call our Macmillan Nurse, Janet.

'I'm really sorry I can't come today,' she says. 'It's my day off. I'll see if anyone else can drop round.'

I feel profoundly bleak, alone and incapable of meeting the responsibility the universe seems to have allotted me. 'Someone's coming to see us,' I say to Michael. 'Let's get you back into bed.'

'I think I might be sick,' he says.

'It'll be okay once you're back in bed,' I say. 'It's all that effort. You need to rest. Remember what Janet said about the energy bucket? Whatever you use, you must top up?'

I help him swivel his legs around onto the bed and then we put our arms around each other and between us, shimmy him up the bed a little way. I straighten his legs out, pull the duvet and blanket over him, find the controller, and lower the backrest so that he is semi-inclined and supported on his freshly plumped pillows. 'Is that better?' I say.

'Yes, a bit bet–' his voice trails off and in moments he's asleep.

10 am

At 10.15 am, there's a knock on the door. It's brusque, efficient Tracy, the Hospice at Home woman here to wash Michael. I don't think she approves of me. I think she thinks I've not been good at Michael's personal care.

When she was here on Saturday, giving him a bed bath, I opened the door to Michael's room and they both turned and looked at me, as if in collusion, as if I'd caught them in flagrante. She had the hospital bed at full height, a bowl of warm soapy water on a stool beside her. She was soaping my husband's naked body, paying particular attention to his genitals. His face bore the uninhibited pleasure of a baby being washed and changed. I felt like an intruder and quickly left the room and shut the door. Had Michael let me, I would have stripped and soaped and washed and dried and changed. I would have done all of this for him, but he refused. I think because there had to be some small way that I was still his wife and not his nurse.

'Hello Michael, it's Tracy. How are we today?' she calls out.

He takes a while to resurface from the depths of sleep, and he tries to say hello, but it comes out like a yawn. He's clearly not up to conversation.

'A bit tired today, Michael?' she asks, overloud, and he nods his head just enough to be noticed.

'Do you want to leave it today, dear?' she says, covering his thin cold hand with her warm fleshy one.

He manages a yes.

'I can come back later if you like,' she says to me, in an exaggerated whisper.

I promise to call her if he changes his mind, and otherwise agree to see her or a colleague the next morning.

Tracy leaves and ten minutes later, there's another knock on the door. This time it is the colleague of our Mac Nurse. He doesn't spend long with us. He is kind and reassuring. We must expect these episodes, he tells us, as Michael becomes more poorly. Such inadequate words to describe what's happening. Poorly. Michael is poorly sick. He is getting more poorly. No. He is dying. That's what is going on. But no one talks about that. No one. Perhaps I am the only one who has noticed how bad things are.

He leaves, and the house is quiet again. It's only mid-morning, but it already feels like a day has gone by.

'How about I make us a fresh drink?' I say, and leave Michael dozing.

When I come back in with our mugs of tea, he is awake. He's opened his A5 spiral-bound notebook with the bright yellow cover that was on the table next to the bed and is moving a pink plastic propelling pencil across the page. 'What are you writing?' I ask.

'I've just remembered something,' he says like someone has dialled him down to slow motion. Holding the nib of the pencil tightly between the tips of his fingers and thumb, he's concentrating very hard on whatever it is, moving the pencil deliberately, with obvious intention. He's written nothing down since Friday, when he last made a note of the 7 pm pills, in handwriting I barely recognised: the steroid dexamethasone for cerebral oedema and to improve his appetite, lansoprazole to protect his stomach from the dexamethasone. Michael moves the pencil up and down, making marks as a child might, if mimicking what he has seen grown-ups do. 'I've got to remember something, on here,' he says. He works hard on the task as though remembering the feeling of letters as they are shaped by the hand and is putting down something of great importance.

We sit together in silence. I'm so tired that even the skin on my face feels weary and for a moment I close my eyes and retreat to an inner place of soft dark where although nothing makes any more or less sense, at least no one is demanding anything of me.

When I open my eyes, Michael has drifted back asleep. With care, so as not to wake him, I extract the pencil from his fingers, slide the notebook out from under his left hand and look at what he has been doing with such effort.

At the top of the page are a series of marks, some long vertical lines and other more solid blocks of graphite, where he's gone over and over the same spot, so the lead has left a small, shining dark rectangle on the paper.

I long to know what he was trying to remember through his slow marks: they are lifelines from another place. They say nothing at all, yet they say everything about what all of this is and how adrift we are.

11 am

I close the notebook, stretching the elastic strap over the smooth cover, shutting in the precious cypher.

Poking the pencil under the elastic I lay the notebook on the bedside table. Michael dozes, oblivious to all of this. Tiredness has bound me to the spot and I'm grateful for it. In the stillness of this moment, I can study him. Ten minutes idle past, or maybe twenty: time slips by unnoticed and unaccounted for.

Although he doesn't look very thin, he looks changed: a faint grey-yellow pallor, a different texture to his skin. Living with the slow increments of decline, I think I've become so normalised to this gradual shapeshifting that I almost don't notice. It's like watching ice melt, the moment of transformation of molecules from solid to liquid being imperceptible but inexorable. Michael is slowly melting before my eyes. Because I know the inevitable conclusion, like I know that water flows downhill, every day feels like a paltry attempt to defy time, to achieve a moment of suspension and turn our backs on the process of disease.

In these drifting times, when nothing much happens, when there are no immediate crises to attend to, no specific demands to meet or behaviours to negotiate, there is still no rest. My organism, my entire being, has become conditioned to the necessity of first response. It is always on. I'm always on standby.

12 pm

A car pulls up outside, filling the air with the low boom of drum and bass, signalling Will's arrival. He's cut holes in the rear parcel shelf to accommodate a massive pair of speakers. Will remains in the car, staring out of the windscreen, his hands clasping the steering wheel as if uncertain about the wisdom of having come to a halt. He wears a look I recognise in myself; on edge, not sure what he needs to prepare himself for, rehearsing the greeting, playing it over in his mind.

We're all beginners at this and have no socially prescribed script to follow.

Will finally gets out of the car and then hesitates for a moment. His long hair looks unkempt, which ordinarily would irritate Michael because he equates it with a certain lack of discipline. What I know is that it's the least important thing for any of us to think about right now.

Shifting from one foot to the other, he puts a hand to his chin and then, decision made, pulls a hairband from his jeans' pocket and makes a ponytail. Then he grabs a well-worn carrier bag from the back seat, his rations for the day. At twenty-nine years old and over six-feet tall, he has hollow legs and eats more than anyone I know. Then, he long-strides towards the house and up the path. He knocks twice on the front door, tentative, like he's still not sure it's the best idea.

Watching all of this from the window has given me a moment to garner my strength. I swallow hard, take a deep breath and put on my smile. I am the family optimist. And early on this journey, Michael made it very clear that the kids were to be protected, that this was our private thing to endure together, so I feel duty bound to honour that.

Truth is, we're all in a state of bewilderment. There are no rules for how to greet your mid-forties step-mum when visiting your dying sixty-two year old father. We're all just making it up as we go along.

I open the front door and greet Will with my best warm and encouraging smile. 'Lovely to see you. How are you doing? Was it a good drive down?'

'Yeah, fine thanks. How's it all going?'

'Your dad's sleepy, but he'll be so pleased to see you.'

Then in a voice more wakeful and clearer than I've heard in weeks, Michael calls out, 'Hi, Will!'

'Hi, Dad!' says Will, dropping the carrier bag in the hall and heading into the front room where Michael has sat himself up in bed, eyes open wide, alert, smiling.

'How are you Will?' he asks, finding the strength from somewhere.

'Yeah, I'm fine thanks, Dad.' says Will, shutting the door behind him.

Left standing in the hall, I listen to their lively chat through the closed door. I feel shut out, like an extra in this drama. By reflex, I go to the kitchen, put the kettle on and make an echinacea and raspberry tea for Will and two builder's teas: one half-full for Michael, one full one for me.

Sukey Cat wanders in from the living room, curls herself around my legs and then slinks through them like liquid. It seems so pathetic, but right now I don't know what I would do without her and Polly Cat. In my mind, I say to her *thank you* and she replies, *we're all in this together, you're not alone.*

1 pm

I head back into the hall with Will and Michael's teas, put one down on the floor, so that I can turn the brass doorknob, then pick it up and shoulder the door open.

Will is sitting on the dark blue sofa, which is where I've slept for the past few weeks, apart from last night, and one-night last week when the Marie Curie nurse stayed over. The room is quite cramped, what with the sofa, my old filing cabinet, two bookcases and Michael's hospital bed.

'Oh, nice one, Fi, thanks!' says Will, as I hand him his tea.

I turn Michael's mug around and holding it with both hands, offer him the handle. He carefully takes it from me, but his hands are trembling and an occasional twitch coming from his right elbow slops the tea this way and that. He brings the mug to his mouth in short jerking movements, takes a sip and then pushes it back to me. Will grimaces. A knock on the front door breaks the tension.

'Ah, it must be Alice,' I say, putting the tea down on the bookcase and getting up to answer it. I don't have to put a smile on for her, at least not in quite the same way.

'Hi, Fi,' she says, stepping in and bending down to hug me. They're all tall, Will, Alice, and Michael. They tower above me. 'How are you doing, sweetheart?' she says.

'We're doing okay, love, thanks. Will's here. He's in with your dad. Do you want a tea?'

'Oh, if that's all right, that would be lovely. Hiiii, Daaaad,' she calls out, walking into the front room. Her voice is so familiar and comforting I could cry, but I don't.

'Hello, Alice!' Michael says. She bends down and gives him a gentle kiss. 'And how are you, my little sweetheart?' he asks.

I go into the kitchen and fill the kettle, looking out of the window at our small garden. There are three separate bays constructed of dry-laid breeze blocks: one containing sand, one gravel and the other hardcore. In front of these is a large mound of topsoil covered with black weed-suppressing fabric. These were going to be something.

I take Alice's tea to her. She's sitting on the bed, holding her dad's hand.

'I think I need to go,' says Michael.

'Okay, love,' I say. 'Can you just give us a minute, guys?' I say to Will and Alice.

'Yeah, sure. Come on, Alice,' says Will, and he and Alice creep around the edge of the bed and out into the hallway.

Left alone again, Michael looks frail and tired. He's been digging deep into reserves to be Dad with a capital 'D'.

'Okay, let's get you up and along to the bathroom,' I say. I lift off the duvet and then between us, we swing his legs around until he is sitting with his feet on the floor. 'I'll raise the bed,' I say, and as I do so it is as though a switch has been flicked, as Michael notices the tube of the syringe driver and I can see his attention drawn to it like a magnet. 'No love, let's concentrate on getting to the loo, shall we? Then Will and Alice can come in again.'

Michael nods and is silent, although he keeps moving the tube between his thumbs and fingers and watching it from the corner of his eye.

Once I've raised the bed, I reach for the sticks and we work together to get him upright, but something has changed since this morning. There is nothing in his legs and regardless of sticks or me easing him up, he cannot stand.

'I've got to go!' he says, sounding desperate.

'Do you want to use the urinal?' This came along with a commode, neither of which we've been quite ready to face.

'No,' says Michael.

But there's no choice. It's not so much the idea of peeing into a bottle that's the problem. We've both done that before, on many camping trips in an ill-equipped and ancient VW camper van. But a medical urinal is something else altogether. It's another cross on the column of things I can no longer do for myself. Admitting it into our life is loaded with emotion and meaning, because we know that this is a one-way street. There's no getting back to normal for us.

I find the plastic bottle, unwrap it from the cellophane, and give it to Michael. He tries to unscrew the lid, but no longer has the grip strength, so hands it back to me. We're awkward with each other, as though we're about to have sex for the first time and now it comes down to it, we're feeling rather uncertain.

Michael puts one arm around me to hoist himself into a better position, and we struggle with his clothing to get the bottle in the right place and at the right angle. It feels all wrong, and the bottle seems enormous next to him.

After much effort, we get everything lined up, and he starts to pee, but with no strength left and uncontrollable twitches in his arms he struggles to hold his position and he and bottle part company. Dark stewed-tea-coloured urine trickles down his leg onto the bed, and a little of it drips onto the floor.

'Oh no!' says Michael.

I hear the living room door being shut. It's too much for Will and Alice to hear. 'It's okay, love,' I say, softly. 'I'll get it sorted. Try not to worry.'

They're hollow words. I feel his embarrassment

and my incapacity to make this better, really better. I go to the bathroom and get a few sheets of loo roll to mop up the worst of the spillage. There's not very much, because Michael has been drinking so little.

'Hang on a minute, I'll fetch some clean pyjamas,' I say.

Michael looks like a child who has just wet his pants at school. Shame and confusion. It is the most painful, most distressing sight.

I head out into the hall, closing the door to Michael's room, so he has some privacy, and open the door into the living room. Will and Alice look up at me, their faces pale and full of concern.

'It's okay,' I say. 'Just getting sorted. We won't be long.'

'Okay, cool,' says Will.

I run upstairs and pull out a clean sheet and clean pyjamas from the airing cupboard. Just for a moment, I hold the fabric close, burying my face in the warm cotton, breathing in the comforting scent of fresh laundry. Back downstairs, I put the clean linen in the front room and fetch a bowl of warm soapy water, a flannel and a towel from the bathroom. I close the door behind me and get busy changing the bed and changing Michael, without him having to stand.

This is as close as I have got to washing my husband and it's a discreet wipe with a warm flannel over his wasted thighs. We stop for a few moments to talk about the syringe driver tube, but thankfully the clean-up is distracting enough to keep his fixation to a minimum.

Though wasted, his legs are heavy as I pick each foot from the floor to ease it through the legs of his pyjama bottoms. His lack of strength is stark. He can barely shift weight from one buttock to the other, but at last, we manage and he is clean and clothed.

Pulling the bed sheet away from the bed, I ease it out from under where Michael is sitting. Then I lower the headrest and between us we shimmy him along to the top of the bed. I put the new sheet on, sliding it over and tucking it under the plastic mattress. Michael puts his arms around me, and I help him get his buttocks onto the sheet and then stretch it over the top of the mattress. Raising the headrest again, between us we slide Michael's legs back onto the bed. He lets the mattress and pillow take his weight and immediately falls asleep as I cover him with the duvet. I wipe up the few drips of urine on the carpet with the flannel and then gather up the soiled bedclothes and take them and the bowl to the kitchen, leaving Michael to rest. The bedclothes and flannel I stuff into the washing machine and then wash out the bowl.

I'm exhausted, not just from the physical effort, but also from holding the weight of inescapable truth. Everything is heading in one direction and there's nothing I can do to stop it.

2 pm

By the time I've cleaned everything up, it is 2 pm.
Will decides to make himself some lunch. I have
no appetite, but he makes enormous sandwiches
for himself and Alice. I take Michael a glass
of water and some fresh pineapple. He is just
stirring. 'Okay, love?' I say.

'Okay,' he says.

It's 2.30 pm by the time Will and Alice finish
lunch and wander back to the front room. 'Hi, Dad,
how's it going?' says Alice.

They sit on the sofa, beside the bed. I return
to the kitchen and clear up the fall-out from the
sandwich making. I can hear the three of them
chatting. Then I'm stopped in my tracks.

'Now, Will, Alice,' I can hear Michael say.
Circumstances may have dimmed him, but he's a

retired academic, a man who could once command a large lecture theatre. Now he's addressing his grown children, in the same sort of voice, albeit quieter, smaller. 'It's time to say goodbye.'

'Dad?' says Alice.

'I want you to promise me you will look after each other, all of you.'

'But Dad...?' says Alice.

'You must promise me you'll look after each other, okay?'

'Yes, of course, Dad,' says Will. He's putting on a brave face, being the big brother, but behind it all, his voice is uncertain, watchful.

I quietly step into the hall and pull the front room door shut to give them some privacy, and tiptoe back to the kitchen. He's saying goodbye, he's actually saying goodbye, I say to myself. Then my head is full of white noise again and I walk into the sound.

3 pm

I reach for the kettle. Limescale crusts the stainless-steel spout. Everything gets like it in this house: calcification, marking time.

The kitchen is a work in progress. When we married and bought the house, Michael told my mum that he had one last project in him. When he retired eighteen months ago, he'd had such plans for the house and garden. He always said the kitchen should be the last piece in the jigsaw. Besides, as he prefers mixing concrete to cooking, the kitchen didn't register as a priority.

There is a hole in the ceiling ringed by a dirty brown stain from a flood in the bathroom above. It's been there for years. Grey grease and flecks of blue household sponge edge the sharp stalactites of Artex across the ceiling, evidence of failed attempts to make the best of things.

The old fluorescent strip-light, that hasn't worked for the past seven years, has a coating of sad little corpses of thunder flies that have met a sticky end in the steamed-grease residue of the evening meals of our marriage.

Ridges of old tile cement, smoothed by layers of white emulsion, scar the walls.

I turn on the cold tap of the mixer. The blue-edged disc has worked loose. I let the water run cool and some of it weeps past the worn-out tap washer. I fill the kettle through the lid, watching little pieces of limescale come loose and drift and swirl, like a rather disappointing snow globe.

The worktop has blown fat behind the mixer block from the chronically leaking washer and the mock-marble laminate has lifted to reveal the blackened, disintegrating chipboard inner.

The tiles behind the sink and on the windowsill are the last remnants of a 1970s kitchen. I'd prised and hacked the others off, with bolster and chisel and crowbar, along with the rotten kitchen units and cat-pee-sodden cork floor tiles during the first weeks after taking possession of the house.

Michael and I had worked together as a team to make our new home habitable and recover it from the neglect of the previous occupants; it was a labour of love. That was seven years ago this month.

How have we lived like this for so long, in this make-do-and-mend kitchen that is impossible to keep clean? Christmas dinners, birthday cakes, romantic suppers, Sunday roasts, family teas: I've materialised all of them out of this unpromising space that now *we're* never going to finish.

I used to be embarrassed about it, about inviting people for supper, but now I'm bone-tired and it's become relegated to something of passing interest, a mere observation, like you might notice a cigarette end in a gutter and feel vaguely sad.

No wonder Michael stays in his bed. It doesn't do to be reminded of the things he can't put right, especially things that would be quite fixable, given time.

I pull myself out of these reflections and notice that Alice has returned to her favourite end of the sofa in the living room. With one hand she is texting, and with the other, she is twirling a fat lock of brunette hair around her fingers, rubbing the soft strands against her upper lip.

Small comforts. She's deep in thought. She's not mentioned her dad's illness to any of her friends, apart from her boyfriend, whom she lives with. I'm not sure why. I don't imagine her to be bound by the same code of silence that I feel compelled to uphold. She lives far from here, in London, so there's no one to mind or know about her telling. Maybe it's self-protection. Perhaps, while she's away, she can imagine that life here goes on pretty much as it always has.

I hear the toilet flush and a door open and then silence for a few moments. Will must be composing himself outside the bathroom door. He slopes down the hall and into the living room.

'All right, Will?' says Alice, and I see the tension in her voice mirrored in his face.

I leave them for a moment to check on Michael. He's fallen asleep again, his mouth hanging open. I can see his tongue furred white. I stroke the back of his hand. It's cold to the touch, so I pull the covers up a little and tuck him in. Small acts to make him comfortable.

I can hear the kettle coming to the boil, so it's back to the kitchen to rinse out the mugs and make another echinacea and raspberry tea for Will and two builder's teas for me and Alice.

I stir each mug of builder's tea twenty times before squeezing out the bag and removing it. It's an act of remembrance of things past. Michael brought me a mug of tea in bed every morning for nearly fourteen years until seven weeks ago, when he became too weak to maintain the ritual. He made an excellent tea and him being a man of method and habit, I several times observed the making and counted the number of times he stirred the bag. A consistent twenty. He can't do it now, so I've adopted the technique.

I take the tea through to the living room and the three of us sit in silence, cupping hot mugs in our hands and staring out of the patio window at the garden as the steam rises from our drinks.

Sukey Cat is sitting on the low garden wall, observing us with a steady gaze. She makes a meow, muted through double glazing, which I mouth back at her. For a moment, I am lost in this silent conversation.

I can't tell if Will and Alice have grasped what the goodbye means. They've not mentioned it and

I don't know if I should. So instead, I ask Alice how work is going.

Since graduating, she's been working a range of the usual out-of-hours city jobs; bars, events. But she tells me she has a new job, working for a national charity. Her working day will now finish at 6 pm, not 6 am. 'Alice, that's brilliant news! Dad must be so pleased!'

'I haven't told him,' she says, a note of defeat and anxiety in her voice.

'But you should. He'll be so proud of you!' I say, grateful to have something so positive to lighten the mood of their visit.

I catch Will and Alice taking sideways glances at the dining table, host to Boxing Day all-you-can-eat buffets, home to hilarious games of Cluedo, Monopoly and cards. The yellow sharps box announces itself: it can't be disguised as something else, nor is its meaning softened. Its truth is categorical, absolute.

I feel so out of my depth and so stupid and helpless that I feel sick. I give them my best shot at an encouraging smile and leave Will and Alice in the living room to process the truth of their surroundings while I check on Michael.

It's 3.45 pm, and he's still asleep. I sit on the edge of the bed and pick up and cradle his left hand in mine. His palm is dry, and on the back, nestled in amongst the filigree of veins that show through tissue-paper skin, are three bruises like squashed blueberries from previous injection sites before they installed the syringe driver.

'Michael, Michael,' I whisper, and he opens his eyes, looking straight into mine, his face breaking into the warmest of smiles.

These moments, which are now so rare, when for a second we seem to have access to what was before, are as breath suspended, tangible as air, then gone.

'What's that?' he asks, picking at something I can't see on the duvet. He extracts his left hand from the embrace of mine to examine the object of his attention between his fingertips, once again pulling a perfect invisible thread from one hand to the other, turning it this way and that. 'Here, hold this!' he says, handing the burden of care for this precious thing to me, before reaching for another on the duvet.

I'm so far from him now, from his way of seeing the world. 'I'll just put it down here,' I say, carefully laying the fine, magical line on the cover before getting up to leave the room. 'I'll let the kids know you're awake. Would you like a tea?', but he's too busy with his picking and sorting to answer.

In these uncertain times, the repetitive ritual of making tea is a great comfort. It's something so unremarkable and dull that I can entirely rely on it. I go back into the kitchen to make Michael a drink and then call Will and Alice to join us.

4 pm

By 4 pm, all four of us are crammed into Michael's room. I use the controller to raise the backrest of the bed until he's more upright and then adjust the pillows and pull down his rucked-up T-shirt and smooth the duvet until he looks more comfortable.

Even with the heating on, Michael can't keep warm, so I help him into his favourite shirt. It was a Christmas present from Alice a decade ago: an open weave fabric of white and pale green stripes with a black abstract pattern in between. The look is rustic South American. First one arm, then around the back, then the other arm, being sure to feed the syringe driver box through first.

Will and Alice are sitting on the sofa bed watching these expert manoeuvres. Will looks embarrassed, Alice pensive.

Will gets up from the sofa, walks around the bed, out of the room, and then up and down the hall a few times before coming back in and regaining his place on the sofa, some personal equilibrium restored.

It feels awkward, sitting together like this, watching Michael sleeping, as though waiting for a sign of something.

5 pm

'Hey, does anyone fancy watching a DVD?' says Alice. It seems incongruous at this moment, but it's also something familiar and something typical for us and it's by far the best idea any of us have had all day.

On the second of the large bookcases in Michael's room is a DVD player and a TV, and on the shelf beneath, a box set of Stephen Fry and Hugh Laurie as Jeeves and Wooster.

'How about this?' says Alice, and it's as if the room has breathed a sigh of relief.

She gets up to organise our viewing and I fetch a dining chair from the living room so we can all sit together and see the TV without having to perch on the bed. It's a relief to have something to focus on that isn't Michael; it takes the pressure off all of us, him especially.

The flurry of activity wakes Michael from his snooze, and he looks around with interest and anticipation. He loves PG Wodehouse. He loves cricket and David Suchet as Hercule Poirot and elegant mathematics and Inspector Rebus and his family and making camping breakfasts of eggs and baked beans with little sausages, and concrete, he really loves concrete. And we're all beaming, just a little, because we all know this and for a moment, he is that man and we can pretend that there will be many more episodes of Michael enjoying the things he loves, of being a person who remembers these preferences and can act on them.

'It was one of those big days for beamers,' Michael quotes as the title sequence rolls on The Village Sports Day at Twing. And that's just what it is, because possibly for the first time in weeks, at least together, all of us are laughing. We're finding farce funny. We're caught up in the pure eccentricity of Bertie Wooster and all those characters with preposterous names like Bingo Little and Stephanie 'Stiffy' Byng and newt fancier

Gussie Fink-Nottle. I feel we're being looked after by Jeeves, that he is our very own 'Personal Gentleman,' a man with cunning solutions to intractable problems.

The mood in the room has shifted from tense and watchful to warm and open. It's a moment full of heart and nostalgia and love.

We watch the episode, Michael laughing, dozing, laughing, dozing until he is fully asleep as the opening sequence rolls on 'The Hunger Strike,' and I turn off the TV.

6 pm

'Is it all right if I have something to eat, Fi?' asks Will, bursting the bubble of the moment as the three of us have drifted into watching Michael dozing, like he's a subject in a sleep research clinic who we're responsible for monitoring.

'Oh, Will—,' says Alice, 'it's all you think about!'

'It *is* 6.15,' he says. 'I'm hungry!'

Despite Alice's protestations, I'm relieved to know that someone in the house has an appetite, as this is evidence of life ongoing. We still need to eat, even if Michael won't.

Will and Alice follow me into the kitchen and the three of us stand around the tall fridge-freezer, looking in at the contents with little enthusiasm. There's a selection of microwavable ready meals: vegetarian cannelloni, lasagne, moussaka, and fish pie. They all look flaccid and unappealing in their black plastic trays and film lids.

'I'll have something later,' I say. 'Let's just get you two sorted.' The longer Michael persists with his rejection of food, the harder it is to swallow. Eating without him feels like a betrayal, tucking into a banquet in front of a starving man.

The last proper meal we shared was on Valentine's Day, and he couldn't finish that. I'd made a special dinner, trying to maintain the ritual of dates and celebrations even in the face of each one being the certain last. He'd put his knife and fork on the plate and pushed it towards me, saying he was sorry, but he couldn't manage it. This was so unlike him that, in an instant, my appetite had evaporated.

The day after that, he'd made his usual breakfast of cereal and dried apricots with a mug of frothy coffee, but most of it had gone in the bin or down the sink. Lunch and dinner that day had followed the same pattern.

We tried various options, but he just fancied nothing. The smell of food made him feel sick and then just the thought of it. After the third day, he could no longer manage the stairs, which is when we both moved into the front room, sleeping on the sofa bed. The fact is, we haven't spent a night together in our own bed since then, but this state-shift happened so fast that the occasion of it went unacknowledged.

I began making a careful note of every calorie Michael consumed, calculating what he was missing and what would need to be made up for the next meal or the next day. When Janet, the Mac Nurse, visited, I showed her the record of missed meals and she upped the dose of the steroid dexamethasone to stimulate his appetite, although the effect was minimal.

That was six weeks ago. To get something into him, anything, I've been preparing fresh pineapple and keeping it in the freezer so that he can have a small bowl of fresh fruit ice lolly chunks to suck on and chew.

Janet suggested we try nutritional drinks for ill people, like Fortisip or Complan, but Michael hasn't liked the flavours or textures or the very idea of them, and there's a stubbornness around his persistent refusal of nourishment. I find myself wondering if he's chosen to bring this business to a close, to defeat the cancer by starving its host. It's a strategy that, at least for now, he's able to execute. It's a part of his life over which he still has agency.

We haven't talked about this. But then we haven't talked about any of it and maybe it's just my tiredness or sense of defeat that has led me to this dark conclusion.

Janet has also given me the official explanation, which is just as plausible: as Michael becomes *more poorly*, he won't want to eat. It's his body saying no because it can no longer process the food.

Whatever the reason, it all feels wrong and runs counter to everything I thought I knew about what it means to take care of someone when they're ill. Until recently, I understood that to be about providing comfort and promoting healing through nourishment, fluids, warmth, and gentle encouragement to rest.

Against this backdrop, I'm pleased that despite everything, Will and Alice are always hungry.

'I'll have the moussaka, thanks,' says Alice, and goes and slumps on the sofa in the living room.

'Veggie cannelloni, Will?' I say.

'Oh, yes please, Fi,' says Will. His voice sits somewhere between his natural diffidence and his total certainty when it comes to food. He joins his sister, and I remain in the kitchen, happy to at least be able to provide nourishment for someone in the house.

I take a clean fork out of the dishwasher and, holding it in my fist, stab the boxes of food, piercing the film lids with sharp, violent pops. The noise and the action are far more satisfying than the contents and are more cathartic than squishing bubble wrap. I could stand there all day, taking everything out on the ready meals.

I open the microwave door, slide in the moussaka and dial in the minutes. I watch the food rotate on the glass plate like it's a display item on the shopping channel and my mind tunes in to random: *is the Welsh name for a microwave really a popty ping? When will all the daffodils in the front border flower? Did Michael really see a small Roman Centurion standing beside his bed the other morning, as he said?* I'm on autopilot during these musings, taking out a hot plastic tray, half-heartedly shaking the contents, and putting it back in for another minute. It's like I've snoozed the alarm and fallen asleep into a fitful dream. When the microwave pings for the second time, I come to with a start. I take out the moussaka and put in the cannelloni.

The cat flap clatters twice as Polly and Sukey fly in for their supper, slinking and curling around my legs and getting under my feet as I move through the familiar space. I dig out more cutlery from the dishwasher, reach for two white plates from the cupboard above the microwave and decant the steaming meals.

They don't look like food, at least not like the food that I make. They are artless spreading pools of processed ingredients, and the smell of hot cheese, fatty and savoury, makes me retch.

Will and Alice won't be eating at the dining table, amidst the sharps and medications and medical notes, so I find two trays and take their suppers in to them. Will tucks in with gusto. Alice absently moves food around her plate as though trying to distract her attention and trick herself into eating something when she's not looking.

It's not long before Will has cleared his plate. 'Thanks, Fi!' he says, already heading back towards the kitchen, 'Are you planning to eat the other cannelloni?'

I feel sick and on edge and buzzing with adrenaline and deeply, existentially, tired. My now-permanent state of anxiety is wearing me so thin that I might just become translucent.

Lovely though it is to have them here, our visits from Will and Alice don't bring me respite, just an opportunity to drive to the chemist on the other side of town to collect Michael's prescriptions, or occasionally go to the supermarket; the only two places I've been outside of the house in the past eight weeks. They are two more people in this drama that I feel I must, and I want to take care of.

There's no one tasked with taking care of me, though, least of all me. 'No, it's fine. Have my cannelloni, Will,' I say. I just can't stomach it.

Alice is still moving food around her plate, but she's gradually getting through it.

'Are you going to tell Dad about the new job?'

'I think so,' she says.

'Well, I think you should. It's such fantastic news!'

She's a bright and bubbly girl, but underneath it all, she seems plagued by deep-seated self-doubt. She needs encouragement - don't we all? And she needs her dad.

In the family dynamic, Michael and Alice are peas in a pod, usually aligned with taste and values. She is his special girl, he's her old Papa. She makes a fuss of him and always finds him a clever present for birthdays or Christmas.

Time was they looked quite glamorous together; She, tall and beautiful, with a cascade of dark brown hair. He, tall, rugged and lived-in. They both tower above me.

Once, walking down Oxford Street in London, heads turned as we passed, not just clocking Alice's striking looks, but Michael too, the dashing appearance of his younger self still clear in his now matured, grizzled sort of handsome. I felt invisible next to them; the small, unremarkable step-mum with genes of an altogether different configuration. I'd give anything to have that moment again, to walk with father and daughter, to watch the way they talk and laugh together, their deep connection and understanding. He calls her 'Alice the Peacemaker', for she has adopted the mantle of family arbiter through years of the usual familial conflicts.

I take Alice's tray, head back into the kitchen, and load her plate into the dishwasher. I've lost track of what is clean and what is not, so some things in there have probably been through the wash cycle at least four or five times. Will follows me out with his plate and begins organising another meal for himself. While he's waiting, he flicks the switch on the kettle.

'You doing okay, Will?' I ask.

'Yes. I'm fine. Thanks, Fi,' he replies in a soft, hesitant staccato, dropping an echinacea and raspberry tea bag into a large blue and white mug he's found on the shelf above the kettle.

Circling the terrain of the kitchen we perform a tango of near misses and collisions as teaspoons are reached for, the fridge door is opened and the microwave attended to, all to an accompaniment of small talk, me looking up at him and him looking down at me with his head to one side. He must be a foot taller: a long neck and long torso extending from the scaffold of legs and pelvis.

7 pm

I leave Will to his second dinner, check in on Alice, who is busy texting, and take Michael a fresh glass of water. He wakes up as I walk in, looking straight into me, soft-eyed. I sit on the edge of the bed stroking the dark hairs on his forearm and then turn his hand palm-up, placing mine palm-down on it. Although I've spent the ten days since Will and Alice were last here wishing we weren't so alone, oh how I now long for it to be just me and him again.

'Here you go, have a sip of water,' I say.

His parched lips are sticking together, making it difficult for him to speak more than a mumble. He puts his hand over mine, gradually brings the glass to his lips and takes a drink. The striped woolly hat he wears in bed has slid up and is perched on his bald head, revealing some of the soft downy hairs that remain after the whole-brain radiotherapy. I ran the clippers over the strays last week and trimmed his beard and moustache, a new feature since he stopped bothering to shave.

I still can't quite take it in, but it was only three months ago that he had a full head of dark hair and was just starting on a new medication, after months of waiting for the go-ahead from the primary care trust.

'Tarceva has proved a real success for many of my patients, especially for brain mets,' the consultant oncologist had told us. 'I'm going to recommend you to the board at the next meeting.'

The waiting had been terrible, knowing all the while the cancer was progressing. The go-ahead finally given, Michael washed down the first tablet on Christmas day with a glass of champagne, for luck, raising a toast in gratitude to the NHS.

He inspected his back and stomach daily for signs of the rash that everyone gets when the drug is effective, becoming more distraught by the day with the absence of red spots. When it still hadn't appeared after three weeks, during which his health had declined, we went back to see the oncologist, who then realized that he'd forgotten to stop the lansoprazole, the drug to protect the stomach lining from the steroids.

As a result, the new wonder drug, the last fragile hope, failed to be absorbed and was as good as useless. This meant that for months, since the last chemo in September, the disease had been progressing unabated and now there was nothing left in the arsenal with which to attack it. We were dumbstruck, left bewildered as it now became clear that no one, not even the oncologist, had our backs. Michael was told to stop taking the Tarceva. The mistake made, he was no longer a specimen of much interest, and they dismissed us from the consulting room.

I can hear Will and Alice talking together and then the kettle being put on. 'Will and Alice will have to head off soon,' I say to Michael.

'Let me see Alice first,' he says.

I go out to the kitchen and take over tea-making duties. 'Have a chat with your dad, Alice. I'll do this.'

She pulls on a thick strand of hair, head tilted to one side, lost in thought, before making up her mind about something. 'Hiiii, Dad,' she calls out as she walks into his room and pulls the door closed behind her.

8 pm

Will and I sit together in the living room. I want it to feel natural, but it feels awkward. We don't talk about Michael, because somehow, we just can't. Instead, we talk about how uni is going (fine, thanks) and how my work is going (it's not going, not since last year). I can't concentrate because I can hear Michael's voice raised and then the door opening and Alice hurrying to the bathroom.

'Sorry Will, I've just got to check on something,' I say, but he is still talking, oblivious to the small volcano that has just erupted in the other room.

Michael is sitting up in bed, looking energised and wild-eyed. 'Alice has got a job as one of those charity chuggers!' he says, spitting out the words in disdain. His voice is clear and strong, his anger intense. I sit on the bed and take his hand.

'She hasn't, love, she's going to work in the fundraising department of a national charity. It's a serious job!'

But he isn't having any of it. For reasons not clear to me, he's furious with her. She comes out of the bathroom, hurries past and straight into the living room.

'Michael, come on. Alice needs to go for her train. Don't leave it like this. She's done really well. You two need to make up.' I get up from the bed to check if Alice is okay.

She's sitting in her coat, sobbing. 'Dad *hates* me.'

'No, no, he doesn't, love. He's just concerned for you, that's all.'

'Well, he has a funny way of showing it,' she says, unconvinced.

Alice and Will haven't seen Michael like this before. Although always prone to a quick temper, these sorts of uninhibited and unkind outbursts are new and have a Jekyll-and-Hyde quality to them. They started when the cancer metastasised to his brain but have become much worse over the last few weeks, exacerbated by the steroids and, probably, the lack of food.

I'm distressed for them to see their dad like this but also in some small part, I'm relieved, because maybe they'll understand, in a way that I'm not sure they have done yet, why I am struggling to cope. Michael's personality has changed. He has become more volatile and his moods and reactions are hard to predict. I don't know from one day to the next which version of him I'm going to get or for how long. And neither does he.

'He loves you, Alice. He loves you very much and wants you to be successful and happy. But he's not himself and has become prone to blurt things out without thinking. Let's patch things up, shall we, before you go for your train?'

9 pm

All the time that Alice and I have been in the living room, Will has been in with Michael behind the closed door and I am dreading what's being said. We can't afford to have fallings out, not now, not when things are so precarious. The door opens and Will calls us in.

'Will's doing very well,' says Michael, looking sidelong at Alice.

It's unnecessary and rather mean, considering his earlier outburst, and Alice's eyes well up again.

'Alice has got to go for her train now love, she's got work in the morning,' I say.

'Come here Alice, my sweetheart,' he says.
She's wary, wondering what's coming next.

'Fi thinks I'm being mean, but I just want you to know that you can do better, and I want you to promise me you will not take this job.'

'It's a great job,' I say. 'Of course she should take it!'

'We'll see, we'll see,' he says. 'there's no need to cry now, Alice, is there?'

Alice's face has changed from warm and loving to steely and cold. Michael has no concept of the impact his words have on those who love him, who desperately need that love returned, to be banked and saved for later emergencies.

'I've got to go now, Dad,' she says. 'I'll see you at the weekend, okay?'

'All right my Alice,' he says, reaching for her hand as she bends down over the bed and plants a small kiss on his forehead.

'I'll walk her to the station,' says Will.

10 pm

It's only a five-minute walk, but it's dark and it's late and I'm glad Will won't let his sister go by herself, at least for this leg of her journey.

I worry about her sitting alone on the train for the hour's ride into London and then the tube, bus and walk back to Lewisham. She'll be lucky to be home by half-midnight, and all that with the memory of the day to carry. I walk them both to the front door and give Alice a hug, which she bends down to receive.

'Let's speak tomorrow,' I say, 'and please, text me when you get home, okay?'

'I'd like to come back for a bit longer, if that's okay,' says Will.

'Sure,' I say, and they both head off down the path. When I go back to Michael, he's dozing again. 'Hey, it's been a good day, mostly, hasn't it?'

He opens his eyes, but he looks completely exhausted. 'Have they gone now?' he asks, his voice tired, small, and babyish.

'Will's walking Alice to the station. He'll be back in a minute. I hope she's okay. She's got a long journey home.'

After a while, there's a knock on the door.

'Was she okay?' I say, closing the door behind Will.

'Kind of...' he says, wincing slightly.

'Hello, Will,' I hear Michael call out, but much quieter than he mustered this morning. The two of us go into the room. Will sits on the sofa and I sit on the bed.

'So, you'll be good, Will,' says Michael.

'Yes, Dad.'

'You'll look after your sister?'

'Yes Dad, that's right.'

'And your Mum?'

'Yes, yes, of course.'

'And Fi?'

'We'll all keep looking after each other,' I say.

Michael is struggling to keep his eyes open. It's been a long day with lots of activity, compared to what has become the norm.

Then apropos of nothing, he opens his eyes wide and starts reaching for something in thin air, as if trying to catch a stray balloon or a blown bubble. Will's not seen him do this before and he looks uncomfortable, shifting in his seat.

'Look at this one,' says Michael, carefully balancing whatever it is he can see on the palm of his hand.

'I can't see it, Dad,' says Will, but rather than dismiss the existence of the object not visible to us, he says, 'what's it like?'

Michael's arm drops to the bed. He looks from Will to me and back as if detecting a conspiracy, his expression describing a mixture of mischief, bewilderment and the deepest, most profound exhaustion. We sit together for a while in a silence that feels awkward until Will makes a move to leave.

'I've got to go now, Dad,' says Will, 'but I'll come and see you again in a few days, probably on Thursday. I'll organise it with Alice.'

'Okay Will,' says Michael, his voice quiet and remote.

Will leans over the bed and hugs his dad as

best as he can and then fetches his bag from the living room and walks with me to the front door. 'See you later in the week then, Fi,' he says.

'Thanks for coming, Will. Check in on Alice, won't you? I will too.'

'Yeah, sure.'

'And I'll call you if there's anything, you know, to report, okay?'

'Yes, okay.'

'All right, love. Drive safe, and hopefully see you on Thursday...' and with that, I reach up and give him a hug.

Will walks off down the path to his car. It's quite mild for the time of year and my breath leaves no trace. I watch red taillights grow smaller as he leaves the village.

Sukey Cat slides past me through the open door.

11 pm

When I close the front door, it is as if the air has been sucked out of the house and sealed us in like vacuum-packed meat. I check on Michael and he's dozed off again. It's been an exhausting day.

I trudge upstairs to our bedroom: the double bed, the curtains I made when we moved in seven years ago, the wardrobe Michael built, the wool rug, and on the wall the framed card of a single red rose he gave me on Valentine's Day morning, the year we bought the house. It was the prelude to a surprise dinner and marriage proposal. A man not given to romantic gestures, this was really something.

I slide open the mirrored wardrobe door and hang up my mauve cardigan, looking again at the little beads on the edging that so fascinated

Michael this morning. It seems like longer than a day. It's a relief to get out of my jeans and into my comfy pyjamas.

Hooked on the back of the bedroom door is the magenta cotton kimono I treated myself to and gift-wrapped as Michael's present to me at Christmas. It has embroidered flowers in vibrant shades of purple, red, mauve and green, and conjures an art déco era Paris or London or New York, my idea of it, anyway. I have only worn it once, on Christmas night, and now I'm moved to lift it off the hook, slide my arms into the wide sleeves and wrap it around my slight frame. It swamps me, but I feel swaddled and comforted.

I sit on the bed for a while with my head in my hands. It's so quiet that I can hear my heartbeat pulsing in my ears. My feet find my slippers, toes kneading the soft fleecy interior. I take out my contact lenses and *put my eyes on*, as Michael calls it, when I don my glasses.

The first thing that comes into focus is the photo on my bedside table. I pick it up, trying to place myself within the time frame.

The two of us on top of a mountain in the Picos de Europa in Northern Spain. Although I love a good long walk, Michael is no mountaineer, so on this occasion, we were on the limestone plateau courtesy of a hair-raising ride in a cable car. You can see the landscape stretching out behind us. I remember the views were long and magnificent that day.

From our viewpoint, we could just see the coast to the North and trace the silver blue line arcing round to the West, towards Galicia and on to Cape Finisterre, the end of the world and the next destination on our tour.

Dots of colour on a square of green, edged with woodland on the valley floor, indicated our campsite and we could just make out our old blue VW campervan by the ancient orange VW Motent awning on the side. I remember it was cold with a stiff wind: Michael is wearing his thick dark blue fleece and I'm wearing two.

It's an old-fashioned selfie, the camera propped out of sight on a rock with the timer set. After I'd pressed the trigger, I'd run back to my spot. I'm flush-faced and wearing a huge smile that's just on the edge of laughter. Michael is holding onto me, having caught and spun me around just in time for the shutter to open. How unknowing we were of what was to come.

That trip was eight years ago, and I wonder if the genes in the cells in his lungs had already mutated, unseen and unfelt, at that point. Was there a moment when all of this could have been treated and dealt with? The uncaught cough.

I've been upstairs for nearly half an hour, lost in these thoughts and aware of the tightness in my shoulders. I put the picture back on the bedside table and consciously try to relax, taking deep breaths, lifting my shoulders to my ears and dropping them down with my out-breath. 'Okay, come on Fi,' I say out loud, and I get up off the bed and walk out of the room with purpose, turning off the light.

12 am

Reaching the foot of the stairs, I sidle past the dining table with its monstrous buffet of medical paraphernalia, turning off the light as I go. Onwards to the kitchen, I take a glass from the dishwasher and pour myself a small glass of Rioja from an open bottle. I take my wine, turn off the kitchen and hall lights, and go into Michael's room. The house closes in darkly behind me. Everywhere are shadows.

Michael stirs as I walk in and we begin the bedtime ritual, later than usual, of readying ourselves for sleep. 'Do you need the loo?'

'No, no, I don't think so,' says Michael, and it's just as well because I'm not sure I'd get him safely out of bed and along to the bathroom, not after this morning. Those times have passed. There is always the pee bottle, but that was a disaster earlier. It's something else to speak to our Mac Nurse about tomorrow.

'Here, love, have a little water,' I say, and Michael takes a few slow sips in the still moments between jerking hands.

On the bookcase is the little bottle of fluconazole for oral thrush. I unscrew the lid and squeeze and release the soft black rubber pipette to suck up a bit of the liquid into the glass tube. Michael opens his mouth and holds out his tongue, which is furred white all over.

'Is it feeling any better?' I ask.

'Uh-uh,' he replies, shaking his head, tongue still out.

I squeeze on the rubber and drip five drops of the liquid directly onto Michael's tongue. His face almost folds in on itself in recoil from the intense bitterness.

What does help is the nightly teaspoon of Oramorph, the liquid morphine prescribed for pain and anxiety, which helps Michael get off to sleep. The dangerous liquor is sweet and potent and instantly soothes. I've tasted it before, but my duty to remain alert is enough to resist the temptation to give in to its narcotic pull and take a big swig from the bottle. My half glass of red serves the same purpose without undoing me.

I lower the head of the bed until it is horizontal, pull the duvet back and straighten the sheet, manually lifting one heavy leg and then the other and then adjusting everything again to smooth out the sheet and pyjamas. Then, with Michael's arms around my neck, I lift him a little to adjust the pillows before I cover him with the duvet, making sure there are no gaps at the bottom of the bed to let drafts in.

All is quiet and still.

'It's been a lovely day, hasn't it?' I say, hoping that it was so, still regretting his upset with Alice, but not minded to dwell on it anymore.

Instead, now that he's all tucked in and comfy, I climb onto the bed, which although narrow can accommodate both of our slim frames. I push my head under Michael's right arm and rest it on his chest, hugging my arm across his body. We lie there like that for a little while, not saying anything, just holding on.

He is the first to break the silence. 'Will they be all right?'

'Yes, they'll be fine.'

'And will you be okay?'

'Yes, love, I'll be okay.'

His questions are small but vast. He doesn't mean now, of course, are we all okay now, he means *Afterwards*.

'We'll look after each other, I promise.' My words feel throttled, bound into tight little balls in my throat. I don't want to think about any of it now, so I snuggle into him, burying my face in his duvet-padded chest, one leg on the side of the bed to hold me in place and stop me from falling off, my arm wrapped around his tummy. We lie in silence, our breathing quieter than the huffing-puffing mattress of the hospital bed. It's like there are three of us in the room.

I read on a cancer care website that when someone is reaching the end of their life, it's important to tell them it's okay to leave behind all that they know and love and to surrender to the inevitable, to give them permission to die so they can let go. At the time I read it, I thought the idea was preposterous and horrifying. If it's that easy to change the course of history with a sentence, how vigilant we need to be with language, how careful not to have a slip of the tongue.

Much as I don't *want* to think about it, not now, not in this moment of closeness, my instinct tells me we're now, very gently, having that conversation, and despite my reservations I have a profound urge to tell Michael that it *is* okay, that he doesn't have to worry, that we're all going to be fine.

I also desperately want to believe my brave talk, but it feels like a bare-faced lie. Michael protects, he solves, he decides, he acts, he provides, and he builds. And yet in this final act he is out of the driving seat, waiting just like the rest of us, not knowing when or how and unable to fully prepare.

My heart is beating hard, as though I'm about to jump off the high-dive board or leap out of a plane. Michael is snoring softly in his throat. I lift my head off his chest and look up into the face that I know almost better than my own. His mouth has dropped open, and he's sound asleep.

'Please don't worry, my lovely one. If you've had enough, if it's time, I understand. We will be all right. It's all going to be all right, I promise.' I say the words, not really believing them and not knowing if he hears them.

Pins and needles develop in my arm and foot and, as carefully as I can, I climb off the bed. Michael stirs, but not much. It feels cold, so I pull the duvet up over his arms. His bed-hat has ridden up again, so he looks like a Smurf, but I don't want to wake him to adjust it.

I sit on the sofa bed, wrap myself in my small duvet, and take a sip of wine. It is rich and dark, and I can immediately feel the alcohol in my belly and then my knees, as though I'm downing a shot of something much stronger.

I sit quietly, watching him breathe and sleep and dream of goodness knows what. I imagine that the cancer, which is both him and not him, has a life of its own. What is it doing now, right now? What other parts of my husband is it invading and consuming? The tumours are already present in his lungs, liver, pancreas, adrenal glands, skin and brain. Wherever next? When will enough be enough? How long will this go on? And then I feel horrified by my last question, horrified and wracked with guilt for even asking it.

It was the same last week with our GP. He was on a routine home visit when I asked him if I should urge Will and Alice to come and stay. What I was asking, but couldn't voice, was whether things were reaching a decisive moment.

He was standing in the living room, next to the dining table with all its paraphernalia, with a look of contempt on his face, irritated by my question. 'It will take as long as it takes!' was his sharp reply, delivered with some force.

I felt ashamed for asking and I felt like a failure for not instinctively knowing what to do when one's husband is dying. I felt useless in the face of it all, not better able to step up to my responsibilities.

The other night in a phone call with Mum, after a particularly tough day, she said, 'you are not responsible for delivering Michael a good death'.

But I am responsible. Michael's choice, his wish, and his decision to die at home have made it my responsibility. His desire for absolute privacy around his illness has made it my singular responsibility. Not talking about any of it, between us or with anyone else, has made mine a solo task of divination.

Watching him now, I am beset with worry and questions. Am I caring for him well enough? How can I get him to eat? What damage is he doing to himself with his refusal of food? What will happen when things move on, when things get worse? Will I be on my own, then? What does 'Hospice at Home' mean, and when will it kick in, or is this already it? In which case, I'm already on my own.

1 am

I look at my watch, and it's late. I wipe away the few small tears that have sneaked through my defences and give myself a stern talking to: Don't be so pathetic. Pull yourself together. Tomorrow is another day. I get stuck on the last one for a moment, and then remember that the district nurse is coming tomorrow and the personal care woman will try again and our Mac Nurse Janet will be back at work and may pay us a visit, and I accept I had better get some rest.

Draining my wine glass, tasting the last drops on my lips, I don't feel great after consuming it, but I feel a bit fuzzy at the edges and my eyes are prickly with sleep. I curl into a ball on the sofa, wrapping myself tighter in the thin duvet, pulling a fleece blanket up over me. I reach out a hand to find the switch and turn off the lamp and then reach for Michael, resting my hand on the bed.

In the dark, I can hear him breathing softly. He's stopped snoring now he's fallen more deeply asleep with the Oramorph. I can hear the bed inhaling and sighing, the pneumatic motor of the air pump humming. In the darkness, my fears crowd in, but I can't keep my eyes open any longer.

I know I am dreaming because I am drifting through endless space, kneeling on a grain of sand, holding onto the edges with my fingertips. In the darkness below me, I can hear a distant roar: the sea smashing onto a shingle bank and drawing the shore back to itself. The sound gets louder and louder until it's all I can hear, and the cacophony wakes me up.

Surfacing from sleep, I realise in horror that the sound is right there with me, in the closed night of the room. In the darkness, I fumble for my glasses on the bedside table and can now make out the shapes and lines of the landscape of our makeshift bedroom.

Michael is breathing hard, like he's been running. Maybe he's been dreaming too. The huffing-puffing mattress is quiet now, in comparison.

Not wishing to shock him awake with the harsh brightness of my bedside light, I get up, edge my way around the end of his bed, and feel for the dimmer switch on the wall. A low glow barely illuminates the room, but it's enough to see what I'm doing.

Michael is moving his limbs under the duvet like a dreaming dog.

'Michael, Michael, are you all right?' I ask, trying to sound calm.

He opens his eyes and looks at me, but I'm not sure whether he's actually awake. He's looking at me but somehow not seeing me. Pulling his arms out from under the duvet, he pushes the covers away.

I sit on the edge of the bed and take hold of his left hand. His grip is firm, and he holds on tight. I find the other hand and now have hold of both. They want to keep moving, as if of their own accord, as if they have free will, rising off the bed like rearing horses, haltered back down to the bed by my grasp, over and over again. 'Are you awake, love?' I say, 'Can you hear me?'

Forcefully, he shakes his hands free of my mine and then grips my arms at my sides. We stay like that for a moment, his eyes searching the room, and then he reaches both of his arms around me, pulling me to him, holding me tight before crying out, 'Help me! Help!' his grip tightening, as if holding on for dear life and afraid that to let go will be to fall fathoms deep.

I hold him close to me, my arms wrapped around his back, stroking, soothing. 'It's okay,' I say, because I don't know what to say. 'Were you having a bad dream?'

'I–I don't know. I don't know what's happening.'

'I'm right here,' I say, as if that's the solution.

He lets go of me and falls back to the bed.

'Let me raise the headrest,' I say, and find the controller so that he can relax without being flat on his back. 'Just try to breathe, slowly now, just breathe, breathe.'

I am talking to him as to a man-child whilst taming and coaxing a wild beast. He's breathing fast again, gripping the duvet, kneading it with both hands, his legs moving beneath the covers like they're bored with all this nonsense and have decided to go off for a walk on their own.

'Michael, can you hear me?'

'Of course I can hear you. I'm not stupid!' snaps his reply, spitting out the words like a bitter pill. There's a strange energy in his voice, almost excitement. 'Well, aren't you going to doooo something?' he says, his voice full of sarcasm, frustrated, shouting.

'Try to relax, deep breaths,' I say. I don't know what this is. Is he having a nightmare, a deep dream from which he can't properly surface?

On Friday, he told me he was afraid to go to sleep. When I spoke to Janet about it, she said it was to be expected but that he was trying so hard not to doze off he would exhaust himself so she would give him something to help him relax.

He wouldn't tell me what he was afraid of, but I could imagine. Not being able to stay awake implied something categorical about the progress of his condition and might be the sleep from which he'd never wake. Yesterday and today, though, he's been dozing off with no apparent apprehension.

'Do you want something to help calm you?'

'Yes, yes, that's it, that's it,' he says.

I reach for the bottle of Oramorph on the bookcase. My hands are shaking so I can't open the stupid child-proof cap. I keep pushing down and feeling the spring yield before turning, but it doesn't turn.

'Come *on*!' says Michael.

And then at last it's open and I measure out 5ml in the little measuring cup and offer it up to his lips. He opens his mouth and I pour in the liquid. He flops back into his pillow and we both wait, a moment of stillness in the room.

'Breathe,' I say, 'breathe. In through your nose, out through your mouth.' I do this myself to give him something to copy until we're breathing in unison. Moments pass in this delicate synchrony. 'Is that any better? Do you want to try to sleep again now?'

'Yes, yes I think so,' says Michael, his voice much calmer, and with that, he closes his eyes and his body visibly relaxes.

I leave the dim light on and slide back around

his bed to the sofa, wrapping my bundled duvet around my shoulders. For a while, I watch him until I'm satisfied that he's asleep. I put my head on the arm of the sofa and close my eyes.

2 am

I am running through a wood in bare feet. Someone is chasing me. It's too dark to see who or what, but I'm terrified. Then I realise it's the dark itself. Now it's crouching on my shoulders and gnarled hands reach around my face and smother my mouth. I try to scream HELP! but my throat won't let the sound out. I try and try again, finally waking myself up with a muffled cry into my duvet, where I have burrowed my face.

I gasp for air. My heart is racing, and my neck is crooked from the awkward position I've slept in. My glasses have pressed into the side of my nose, leaving a painful dent. I take a moment or two to come around and figure things out. I look over at the bed. Michael is wide awake, looking around him, picking at the duvet. 'Are you okay, love?' I loathe my capacity for asking these stupid questions. What do I expect him to say? I feel so dumb in the face of what's happening.

'I can't get them all,' he says.

'The threads?'

'What threads? There aren't any *threads*,' he snarls. He sounds so pissed off with me.

'What then? What can't you get?'

'These men,' he says.

'Men?'

'Yes! Look! These tiny men dancing about,' he gestures. 'They're all over the fucking bed!'

At that moment, Polly cat wanders into the room, making her chirruping meow.

'Come here Polly,' says Michael, his voice teasing, almost seedy. 'Come here and show me your pink arse!'

We're usually deep in sleep by this time of night. I don't know where he's getting all this energy from, especially after the long day. 'How about a drink?' I say. 'Or some water? It's really stuffy in here. Maybe you've overheated, and it's given you nightmares.'

'What are you trying to say?' says Michael, with heavy sarcasm in his voice.

'Nothing love, it's just, I—well...'

'I don't want a drink. I want you to DO something.'

'What can I do? What do you need?'

'I don't know!' he shouts. He breathes hard again, his head moving from side to side like he's scanning the room for an explanation.

'Shall I call the district nurse?' I say.

'I don't know, I don't know, I don't know,' he says, his hands working the duvet.

'Okay love, I'm going to call the district nurse, and see if she can suggest something.' I decide on this course of action because I can't call 999. If I did, paramedics would arrive in half an hour or maybe longer, bundle him into an ambulance and take him to A&E. What else could they do? There wouldn't be a bed, so he'd wait on a trolley, maybe a blue or green curtain pulled around him for privacy, if he's lucky. He'd be incoherent and confused, and I'd be giving a potted history of his medical condition, where we're at, brain mets, all the rest. Eventually, if a bed could be found, he'd get admitted to a ward full of strangers where a registrar on night duty would come and see him, prescribe something, and wait until morning. If we do that, we're not coming home and it's all over.

I go into the living room, put on the overhead light and open the blue folder on the dining table, turning to the list of Important Numbers at the back. There's an out-of-hours number for the district nurses, people that know him, know us. I grab the receiver from the base and dial. The phone rings and rings—*come on, come on*—I say under my breath. Eventually, a woman answers.

'Hello, nurse on call.'

'I'm calling for my husband, Michael. He's under your care. He's woken up very agitated, and he seems very unwell. I've given him some Oramorph, but it hasn't helped. Can someone come out?'

'What's his hospital number?' she asks. I give her the number and the address.

'A nurse will call you back within an hour.'

'An hour? But he's really not well!'

'I've marked it urgent. Thank you.'

The line goes dead. I keep hold of the receiver

and go back into Michael's room. He looks at me, his eyes pleading for answers. 'It's okay, lovely, I've called and someone will phone back shortly.'

I sit on the side of the bed and take his left hand in mine, cradling it in my lap and stroking the dark hairs on the soft edge. He has calmed down and we sit together in companionable silence until he drifts off to sleep. I gently place his hand back on the bed and pull the duvet up over his arms and chest to keep him warm.

I watch the clock, counting the half hour, then 45 minutes since I called. When the display on the handset dances into life, the ringing wakes Michael with a jolt.

'Hello?' I say.

'Hello, it's Carol. How can I help?'

'It's my husband, Michael. He's having a difficult night. He's been waking up very agitated.'

'Has he had anything?'

'Yes, he's had 10ml of Oramorph: 5ml at around midnight and another 5ml at around 2 am. It's had little effect. I'm not sure what to do. This hasn't happened before.'

'I'll drop round and see you,' she says. 'I'll be

with you in about twenty minutes.'

'Oh, okay. Is there no chance of–?' but the line clicks dead before I can finish my sentence.

Michael is watching me.

'The district nurse is coming over,' I say. 'I'm sure she won't be too long.'

In the dim light, the hollows of his cheeks make dark shadows on his face. We clipped his beard last week, and the moustache that had flopped over his top lip. The personal care woman was supposed to do it and tidy up the straggles of fine baby-soft hair on his scalp, but she refused, citing health and safety and things not being in her remit. I thought this strange at the time, given the intimacy of the other care she provides.

Michael has always shaved using a traditional razor and brush and shaving soap. I remember lying in bubbles in the bath at the old flat before we bought this house. I was sipping a glass of Merlot, the yellow flame of a scented candle reflected in the glazed white tiles, watching him shave. First, he dipped the badger-hair brush into the basin and then rubbed it into the hard, white stick of shaving soap, turning it into a thick lather. Then, he took the brush to his face and foamed his cheeks, upper lip, chin, and neck, covering the grizzled sandpaper of dark growth. Next, with the razor in his right hand, he dipped it into the basin, pulling the skin on his right cheek taut with his left fingertips. He stopped at that moment, shaking water from the razor, considering the next move, before, with a practised stroke, he cut a wide stripe through the foam. I remember the sound of the little bristles yielding to the cut and how the foam, shaken clear of the razor, would float in white hair-spiked globs in the warm water. The next cut, and the next, described the methodical habit of the twice daily shave, each morning and evening. The smell of Imperial Leather and the stretch of his top lip over his teeth. Working around to the left-hand side. Finally, pushing his chin towards the mirror, clearing his neck with a series of upstrokes. Warm water splashed onto his face, then cold from the tap. Soft towel dabbing. 'You've left some soap in your ear, silly,' said with fondness. His dark eyes in the mirror, his cheeky wink at me lying in the bath.

Last week I bought a comb and a small set of clippers to do what the personal care woman couldn't or wouldn't do and although he won't let me wash him, he let me try to do something with the straggle of beard and wisps of hair. He kept still while I used some fine scissors from the first aid kit in the drawer upstairs and snipped the whiskers clear from around his top lip. I wasn't confident with the clippers, afraid to cut or jab the teeth into his tender skin, but by the time I'd finished, although not clean shaven, he looked tidy, and he said he felt better.

Michael's beard has grown back in a flecked-sand mixture of ginger, white, black and grey. I reach over and stroke one cheek with the back of my fingers, feeling the hairs softer than I expect and then, with my palm stroking the other cheek, remember the feel of Saturday nights and Sunday mornings in the deep archive of my skin.

3 am

At 3.10 am, I hear the low rumble of a car engine and then watch headlights sweep across the wall above Michael's head. He's been still since Carol called back and I feel sure we're probably wasting her time. What remedies will she have for a bad night's sleep? Warm milk? Chamomile tea? A bedtime story?

She doesn't knock quietly and I dash from the bed to the front door to let her in before she knocks again. It's such a quiet street, day and night, that when there is a disturbance of any kind, everyone hears it. In our private drama that can admit no one, we mustn't draw any attention to the house. Michael will hate it.

Carol is a stocky, tired-faced woman in her forties, wearing a maroon tunic and black polyester trousers.

'In here,' I say, and she follows me into Michael's room, sits on the bed, and takes his hand.

'Hello, Michael, what's going on then?'

'Hello,' he says, all soft, polite and gentle.

'Are you feeling a bit agitated, dear?' she says, in a slow, loud voice.

'Yes, a bit,' he says, gifting her a smile.

She turns to me and says, 'I'll check his syringe driver and see if we can give him something,' and then gets up off the bed and uses the controller to raise it to workbench height.

Michael is passive as she pulls the syringe driver out of the bag that is hooked over the head end of the bed. The storm that arrived two hours ago has passed and I long for her to make the adjustments to the dosage and leave so that we can get back to sleep and put the night behind us. Janet is coming tomorrow and the personal care woman will be back. Things will feel better in the daylight.

Carol unbuttons Michael's shirt and firmly but gently eases his left arm out of its sleeve, feeding the syringe driver box through, and then lifts his loose T-shirt to reveal the clear adhesive pad holding the blue butterfly needle and line in place.

'That all looks fine,' she says to Michael, and he smiles again, a simple, grateful smile.

She takes a key from her pocket and unlocks the plastic box and presses buttons on the keypad until the device makes three short beeps and then another three and then a longer one. She takes a line clip and pinches the line shut and then removes the line from the syringe.

'Right, I'll set up a fresh syringe and give him some midazolam. That will help with the agitation,' and with that, she heads off to the living room.

I hear her putting her medical bag on the dining table with a thump and opening the clasp. Then the slap of the cover of the blue folder as it flaps open onto the table and pages being turned. The rustle of paper and cellophane as she opens a new syringe and takes out a fresh needle.

She is taking her time, considering things, writing things down, and in her absence, Michael starts kneading the duvet, gripping it until his knuckles are white and releasing and gripping again. He takes deeper breaths, his chest rising and falling, his breaths coming faster.

'Where is she?' he asks, and then Carol comes back into the room with two prepared syringes.

She refits one of them into the driver, taps something on the keypad, and locks the box shut. 'I've increased the diamorphine for now. I'm also going to give you a little injection.' She takes the other syringe, already prepared with a needle, and a small phial from her pocket.

'What is it?' I ask.

'It's the midazolam,' she says, as she draws the liquid into the syringe, flicks it with her thumb and forefinger and then squirts a little of the liquid from the needle. She takes a pad of cotton wool from her other pocket, rubs it on Michael's left arm, and pushes a needle into him. He doesn't notice.

'That should help,' she says, feeding the syringe driver box and Michael's arm through the sleeve of his shirt. She puts the syringe driver box back in its bag and uses the controller to lower the bed. 'I'll just write this up,' she says, and heads back to the living room.

Michael is still clutching and releasing the

duvet and is now moving his head from side to side, scanning the room again.

It's just a minute or two before I hear the folder snapping shut and the chair being pushed away from the table and Carol comes back into the room, her bag packed.

'That should be fine now. Any problems, you know where we are.'

With that, she marches to the front door, opens it and doesn't look back as she strides away.

Something vital gets sucked out of the house every time someone leaves, and tonight in its place there's just this muffled grey sort of silence in which I am almost sure I can hear voices. Then I'm certain I can, for it's Michael talking to himself, animated, chattering. I move quickly back into his room and sit on the bed, resting my hand on his thigh. 'How are you feeling, my lovely one?' I say.

He looks at me and then grips my wrist with his left hand. 'Look! Look!' he says.

'Look at what?'

'The grid. In there!'

I stroke his thigh with the other hand, trying to

make calming, reassuring movements.

'I'm in the matrix. Right in it. It's dark but the lines, they're bright green lights, in a grid.' The words are hurrying from his mouth, urgent, tumbling and tripping up over each other. He grips my wrist and uses the grip to lift himself towards me and, with his other hand, starts pointing at the dark cave of the bookcase. 'In there!' he says, breathing fast, moving his head again from side to side.

I'm frightened and out of my depth. If he'd been drunk or high, rather than desperately ill and on a cocktail of morphine and steroids, I would feel more equipped to deal with this. It would be within my sphere of experience and understanding. I would expect it to pass and would be able to reassure and talk him through, asserting that whatever is happening it is because of whatever he's taken. Like I'd done with friends over the years, when they'd been too indulgent and panic and paranoia had set in. After one crazy party, I remember putting a friend to bed. Tucking her in like a child, I firmly and calmly reminded her that once whatever she'd taken was out of her system, the hallucinations would pass. I sat with her and I left the light on because she was afraid. I kept vigil. That was fifteen years before meeting Michael. So long ago.

This is different, though. I can't be sure what's going on. I don't know if it's the brain tumours or the medication or both, but there's no getting it out of his system.

'It's okay,' I say, 'I'm here. Don't be afraid. Whatever she's given you, it hasn't helped. I'm going to call again.'

'Yes, yes, call her. But watch those lines going up and down. Up and down.'

'Let go of my wrist, darling, I need to fetch the phone.' His grip is powerful and I have to prise open his fingers so that I can get up off the bed and go into the living room. I pick up the receiver, press redial and wait as the ringing trills into my ear.

I don't know where the nurses are based, but I imagine a squat 1970s flat-roofed concrete building with inset panels in municipal blue, corridors floored with that foul-smelling, buffed and polished old linoleum and fluorescent strip lighting. The longer the phone goes unanswered, I picture an abandoned nurses' station and the building in darkness except for some emergency lighting.

I walk through to Michael's room. He looks up at me, eyes wide with energy. Why the hell aren't they answering? Then at last we're connected.

'Hello, nurse on call?'

'I'm calling again about my husband, Michael. Nurse Carol came out to see us. She gave him some midazolam and then left. It's had no effect. She said to call again if there were any problems.'

'And what is the problem, dear?'

'Well, he's no better. He's got worse. He's getting more and more agitated.'

'All right dear. A nurse will call you back within the hour.'

'An hour? But it's urgent! Please. Can someone call me back as soon as possible?'

'I've marked it urgent.'

'Thank you,' I say into silence, as she has ended the call.

Feeling utterly and completely desperate, but not wanting it to show, I have the few short strides between the living room and Michael's room to compose myself. I sit on his bed and say in my most reassuring voice, 'Someone is calling back. I'm sure it won't be long.'

4 am

I'm waiting for the phone to ring. Waiting, waiting, waiting. Michael is chattering to himself, picking at nothing on the duvet. 'What is it?' I say.

He looks straight into my eyes, holding my gaze for a few long moments. 'Shapes,' he says, 'pink ones, blue ones, dancing men.'

He has bent his knees, drawing his feet towards him, his left knee drifting from side to side. I reach over and rest my hand on his shin, feeling the movement through my arm, into my shoulder.

The memory of holding hands in the winter, arms swinging as we walked. His woollen overcoat. Our breaths combined in misty traces in the space around us. Leaf litter. The cock pheasant that broke cover as we stomped past, feathers beating the air, making us jump.

The phone ringing to life jolts me to attention. 'Hello?'

'It's Carol. How can I help?' in a voice weary and not just a little irritated.

'After you left–well, he's no better. I don't know what to do.'

'He's no calmer?'

'No, he's no different.'

'Are you sure?' she says.

'Of course I'm sure!' I say. *'What's wrong with this woman?'* I think. 'He's no better. If anything, he's worse. He hasn't settled since you left.' Silently, I add– *'And why the hell did you leave us, anyway?'*

'Well, I don't know what I can do. I'll have to speak to the doctor at the hospice and see what he suggests,' she says. 'I'll call you back, all right dear?'

'Well okay, but please–,' and the line is dead, again.

At this moment, I start to doubt my sanity. I wonder if I am the one hallucinating and if tiredness is unearthing paranoia. Perhaps I'm stuck in a hyper-real dream and at any moment a purring cat pressing her nose to my cheek will wake me up. I'll open my eyes to morning sunshine seeping through the crack in the curtains, as it does in that room, and Michael snoring softly beside me.

'It's that one!' yells Michael, 'In there!' He's pointing at the bookcase.

I follow the direction of his outstretched finger and look over at the dark-glossed spines of hardback cookery books on the shelf. I look back at him and he is scanning the room again, his eyes reaching into every dark corner and resting there before taking wide glances across the walls. Now he's moving his arms and legs, climbing invisible stairs. When the phone rings again, he's stopped in his tracks, distracted by light and sound.

'Hello?'

'Hello dear, it's Carol. I'll come round. The doctor is busy. He's going to call me.'

'Oh, okay, thanks,' I say to Carol. 'The nurse is coming to see us again. She won't be long,' I say to Michael.

'Righty-ho,' he says, 'jolly good,' his voice sarcastic, mocking.

Earlier today, I felt I was being toyed with. I feel it again now. Michael's raving behaviour is like the wind that blows, blows, blows, then stops dead, as though someone has turned off a fan.

He is still calm when I hear a car approaching and see the headlights swim across the room. The car door slams shut, footsteps crunch up the path and then a loud knock. I hop off the bed and scoot swiftly to the front door. Carol walks in, straight past me and into Michael's room.

'I can give him another 5ml of Midazolam, but anything else will have to be prescribed by the doctor,' she says.

She prepares a syringe and then pulls the duvet down a little, reaches into the warm nest of the bed, pulls down the front of Michael's pyjama bottoms to expose some upper thigh and presses the needle in. This time, he notices and winces in pain. Then, before she can reorganise his clothing and duvet, he grips the folds of cloth in clenched fists.

'Okay Michael,' she says, 'Let's get you tucked

back in.' And to me, 'I'll pop over to the hospice and see if I can find the doctor.'

5 am

For the second time tonight, Carol leaves us alone.
Michael is no calmer. Whatever she's given him, it
isn't working for whatever has gone wrong. Time
has become elastic. In the spaces between these
moments of connection with the outside world,
the minutes have become extruded, stretched out
into long sinews of waiting.

I picture Carol driving across town. At this
hour, there'll be no traffic, but it will still take
fifteen minutes to get there. Then she must find
the doctor and explain what she needs. The doctor
will have to prescribe something, goodness knows
what, and Carol will have to fulfil this from the
hospice dispensary. Then fifteen minutes to drive
back, which means at the best she'll be back here
by 5.45 am.

I feel completely powerless, unable to do anything to help Michael calm down. I want to reboot him, just find a magic combination of words to bounce him out of this groove. My helplessness and despair merge into a wave of desperate anger. What is that nurse doing to him? It's not helping. After everything we've been through, all those points of no return during the last year, I have no answers for this. Michael's condition is oscillating from bad to extreme. In his agitated state, he clasps his left hand around my wrist, gripping the duvet with his right. 'I don't want to die!' he shouts. 'I don't want to die!' He's possessed of a power and energy he's been lacking for months.

Although sitting on his bed, I feel a well open beneath me into which I fall so fast that my chest is in my mouth and my head has wings. As fast as I am falling into this deepening place, I become aware of my white-knuckle grip on the bed, holding on with all my strength. Michael is holding onto the duvet with one hand, holding onto me with the other and I'm holding on to the bed: we're skydivers in freefall. I clench my teeth together hard and try to slow down my breath.

'You'll feel better soon,' I say. 'Carol will be back with something to help you.'

'I'm in the network. Can't you see it? The matrix of green lines? I don't want to–'

'Try to slow down, breathe.'

But it's no good. It's like he's the power centre of an electrical storm.

I don't notice the car engine or headlights before the loud knock on the door. I release myself from the raft of our bed and run to let Carol in.

'Doctor has prescribed Nozinan. It's a stronger sedative that will help with his agitation. We'll put it in your arm, Michael,' she says, and begins to untangle him from his shirt and syringe driver, unravelling him like she's working backwards towards a dropped stitch.

She prepares a syringe, turns his inner arm towards her and rubs hard to find a vein, before pushing the sharp steel into his skin. I expect an immediate cessation of frantic activity, but nothing happens, nothing at all. Carol lifts his T-shirt to inspect the butterfly needle from the syringe driver. Blood has seeped out from the site of entry and is leaking out between the folds of skin and the clear adhesive pad. 'Oh dear,' she says, 'let's sort that out.'

It was fine, and now it's not fine, and there is no explanation.

She uses a clip to grip the plastic line shut and with a swift rip that makes me wince, she pulls off the adhesive pad, nearly yanking the needle out with it. She presses a ball of cotton wool over the entry site as she removes the last of the pad, taking a few chest hairs with it. Michael is oblivious. Things are happening to him he can neither control nor understand.

Carol gathers up the syringe driver, plastic lead, needle, pad, and cotton wool and takes the bloody bundle into the living room. 'Right,' she says, somewhat exasperated, 'I'll go and reset all of this with a fresh syringe, and we'll find another site for it,' as if Michael has bled deliberately and messed things up.

I feel like we've done something wrong, getting her out on call unnecessarily. I can hear Carol in the living room, fiddling with things on the dining table, flicking through the blue folder, clicking, wrapping, undoing, and sighing. What is she doing? Why isn't she in here looking after Michael? I don't know what I'm supposed to do. Minutes pass, and minutes more.

Michael is breathing hard. I am mute. I sit on the bed, holding his leg, and stroking it. Things are being moved from place to place on the dining table, and the sound of them reaches me like the decay of an echo. He's panting like he's sprinting, panting like something I've never heard before; sharp, stabbing in-breaths that have no reciprocal out.

'Shush my lovely one,' I say, stroking his leg, but I don't think he can hear me.

Then his mouth is open, sucking everything he can from the air. The open oval of his effort, his chest heaves with the force of it until it is full.

Things are hurtling downhill at a new speed, and I've got no brakes.

The deep brown marbles of his eyes roll upwards into his skull as if seeking answers in the wronged furls and whorls of his brain.

What is this? What's happening, when all I can see of those dear dark eyes is the terrible white?

Then, as fast as they rise, they drop back to

their proper place, landing with a slight bounce, like the reels on a fruit machine land. His sharp, quick-as-a-fox browns are now black holes.

My breath has left me.

I'm in that dream again, silently screaming HELP until my voice breaks out–

'NURSE, NURSE, HELP, QUICK!

I

I

I think

he's–

gone.'

The impermeable membrane of me that has resisted everything thrown at it this past year tries but cannot repel these words or shake them off to the ground.

They are spits of hot oil landing on silk.

They are in me and now they are out of me and they can't be unsaid.

Carol moves from the living room with modest haste and sits on the other side of the bed, taking Michael's right hand in hers, feeling for his pulse with the other. I keep holding his leg. I'm frozen in this hopeless moment.

Michael's breathing slows from a pant to a slow gasp to nothing.

Nothing.

Carol strokes his hand.

My vocal cords may as well have been ripped out, for I can say nothing. I can say nothing at all.

He takes a short, sharp breath.

Then nothing.

Nothing.

Then one more.

Then nothing.

Nothing.

Nothing, for long enough to know that there will be no more.

Long enough to be in the full knowledge that it was the last.

A knowing confirmed by the lights of his eyes going out in a way that I would never have believed possible until now as I watch Michael's perpetual spark of aliveness, the evidence of his whole life's presence, the fact of it, grow dim and dimmer until it is gone and there is nothing but a deep dull milky cloud in his eyes.

'He's gone,' says Carol to me. She's matter-of-fact,

nonchalant, even. And then, as if announcing to the room, 'Michael passed away at 6 am.'

6 am

Michael is frozen in the rage of his leaving, his mouth open, eyelids partially closed over his strange eyes. His limbs are a freeze-frame of a man in flight, a man jumping from a cliff into an unknown place.

I'm open-mouthed, speech fails me. All I can manage is a faltering 'I, he, I.' Carol looks at me, her eyebrows raised in surprise.

'Haven't you been expecting it?' she says. She puts Michael's hand down on the bed. 'I'll give you a moment while I do the paperwork.'

He is monstrous. Him, but not him. Yes, I'd been expecting it but in some future place, not now, not like this, not this electrical storm that just blew itself out before I'd realised what it was, before I'd even said goodbye.

He is warm. If it wasn't for the half-closed eyes opening into nothing, I'd believe he had dozed off, like all the other times, and would before long wake up and be some version of himself, maybe not like before all of this started, but something nonetheless real, corporeal, vital.

Oh, Michael, oh, my lovely one, my life. My hands on his hands, on his face, on his chest, are getting nothing back.

Carol comes into the room with a mug of tea and hands it to me, but not by the handle. The china is scalding. I take a sip and it is hot and sweet.

'I'll sort him out,' she says.

I get up off the bed, wiping my eyes on my dressing gown, not sure what such sorting can mean, not now.

First she turns off the mattress pump that has been huffing and puffing in Michael's new absence and pulls the duvet free from his body, then lowers the head of the bed until it is horizontal. Then she moves to the end of the bed and, taking hold of his ankles, pulls him down, the sheet sliding along the plastic mattress making the task easier, unbending the kinks in his knees, straightening him into a line. She tucks each arm neatly along his side with palms facing down. She takes hold of his head in both hands and moves it this way and that, coaxing it into a tidy centre on a single pillow.

She tries to close his eyelids, but they won't yield as if, despite everything, they can't quite let go of the light. She pushes his chin up, but his mouth drops open. It is a cry, a wide yawn, it's disbelief. It is bewilderment that won't be disabused of its question. She pulls up the duvet, places the other pillow on his chest and uses this to push up and hold his chin in place and then uses the duvet to strap the pillow tightly to his body. He looks strangely swaddled, wrapped in a protective layer, although he's no longer in need of any protection. 'Is there anyone I can call?' she asks.

'Er, I–I don't know.' I can't take this in. I need more time to grasp the rules of this new questions and answers game.

'Okay dear, well, I'll let the doctor know as he'll have to issue the death certificate.' I've got so many things I want to ask her, but before I've been able to articulate anything, she picks up her bag from where she'd put it by the front door and leaves us alone.

Carol's abrupt departure has demolished what little rudimentary scaffolding was in place. Michael is the patient, or he was, and her job is done. I rest my forehead against the cool UPVC of the front door. I am no longer necessary, and I have nothing to hurry for. What there was of us, of this life together, just vanished in the briefest moment that was the difference between life and death, and I have no more understanding of that enigma than I did before the witnessing of it.

Eleven months since the X-ray last April, that revealed a 'shadow on the lung', the CT scan, biopsy, PET scan, oncology appointments, chemotherapy, blood transfusions, whole brain radiotherapy, medications, bad news, worse news, hope given, hope dashed, these last awful weeks; when it finally came down to it, life was impatient for its ending. Michael wasn't ready, and neither was I.

I walk back into Michael's room, and he doesn't stir. He is refusing to fully close or fully open his eyes. I sit on the sofa bed and reach under the bedclothes to find his right hand. It's still warm. I touch his chest. Nothing gives. He is a solid mass of unyielding, unresponsive flesh and bone beneath my disbelieving palm. Despite Carol's attempts to lay him out neatly, the traces of fierce, raging reluctance to leave are still etched in his face, the slant of his eyes, the set of his jaw.

7 am

Although I am not religious, I am consumed with the idea that Michael's soul might be trapped in the room, desperate to get out now that death has freed it from the ailing prison of his body.

I open the curtains, pull up the bamboo blind, and the early sun lands on my face. In the front flower bed, which is already starred with pale yellow primroses, the first daffodil of the year looks like it might just bloom today.

A man with short dark hair runs past the house towards the station wearing a light raincoat that is flapping open, and a pale blue tie that has blown over his shoulder. It's the same colour as the one Michael wore on our wedding day. The briefcase he carries swings heavy and awkward. He's late, but he might just make the 7:08 to Liverpool

Street. I can do it in four minutes if I walk fast, maybe three if I run part of the way. A car drives along the road towards the house before turning left up the hill and meeting another coming in the opposite direction. It's a stalemate for a moment or two until the first car whimpers and lets the second one through. *Don't you know what's just happened in here? Don't you realise my husband is dead?*

In our house, everything is on pause. Outside, nothing has stopped moving.

I turn the latch on the right-hand window and open it wide. A blackbird lands in the blossom budded cherry tree, calling to its mate, and then hops to the ground, rummaging for grubs in the soft spring soil before rising triumphantly, with a writhing earthworm clamped in its yellow beak.

'Go now, love,' I say to Michael., 'Nothing can hurt you, not anymore. It's all going to be okay.'

I picture a cloud of ectoplasm rising from his body and floating with purpose out of the window and into the wide-open sky. A peacock butterfly, woken early from its hibernation by the first spring sun, rests on a branch of the cherry tree, warming its wings into the morning light. When I close the window, it flies away.

I turn to look at Michael. He hasn't moved. He has nothing to say.

I am an empty vessel, spent and tired.

In this new world order, my boundaries of selfhood have become a permeable membrane between me before Michael's death, and me after it, which I don't yet have any clue about whatsoever. I have become insubstantial, passing through this membrane, back and forth, drifting from room to room in our hallowed home like a ghost of what was. There are things I must do. I must make calls to inform people that Michael has died, but a shot of adrenaline erupts into my belly and chest at the thought of it. If I tell anyone, anyone at all, it will all be over, for good.

The cordless phone handset is still where I left it on the bookcase in Michael's room. I pick it up, walk into the living room, and sit on the smaller of the two sofas. I look for Mum and Dad's number on redial and call.

'Hello love?' says Mum. I'm calling so early in the day that she already knows it's bad news, and I can hear that knowing in her voice.

'Mum, he's gone,' I say, pushing the words out before my voice crumples in on itself like scrunched paper.

'Oh, love, I'm so sorry—we're leaving now. We'll be with you as soon as we can. We should get to you by midday. Okay, love?'

'Okay,' I say, and hang up. I put the phone on the coffee table, get up from the sofa and go in to see Michael. 'Mum and Dad are coming. They'll be here by midday,' I say to him.

I find the next number on redial.

'Hello Fi?' says Alice.

'Alice, I'm, I'm so sorry, but it's Dad. He's gone.'

'Oh, sweetheart, no. How? I mean, what happened?'

I'm unprepared for her reasonable questions and finding it hard to form words and let them out, I just don't know what to say to her. I feel Michael's influence and my reluctance to upset or burden her, but why? Why not be upset? Her father has died. Should she not be able to wail and beat her chest at her loss, rather than me wrap her up in a quasi-protective coating? 'He woke up in the early hours feeling poorly and it all happened quite suddenly. I called the district nurse, and she was here. I'm so sorry, love.'

'Do you want me to come down?' she says.

I don't know if she's offering to help or asking permission. I don't know if she wants to see him, as he is now, or not, and I can't make this decision or start that conversation now. There are so many moments where the wrong thing said or done changes the world forever. I feel overwhelmed with the responsibility and unable to carry it anymore. 'It's up to you, Alice,' I say. 'Mum and Dad are on their way. I won't be on my own.'

'Okay, so I'll talk to work and come later in the week then,' she says, and a pause and then in a smaller, quiet voice, 'thank you for looking after my dad.'

At which I mumble something soothing and hang up, unable to formulate anything coherent in response or contain my emotion. 'I've told Alice,' I say to Michael.

I can hear his reply, clear as anything, 'She's a

good girl.' But he is still unmoving.

My next call is to Will. He is watchful, thrown. His voice adopts a sombre, bad news receiving tone; his measured, careful words are taut.

'I'll come down, shall I? Today? Or I'll come later in the week.' He is speaking in the sort of voice you'd expect, but somehow it isn't his voice, and this is unsettling.

I tell him I won't be on my own, that Mum and Dad are coming. He doesn't ask about Michael, not when or how or what happened, so I just say, 'All right Will, I'll see you later in the week.'

'Will you be okay?' he asks.

'Yes, I'll be okay,' I say.

'I've told Will. I think he was all right.' I say to Michael.

Michael looks doubtful. Well, he doesn't, of course, but the way I render him in my imagination, his mouth moves, his eyes move, and words come out.

'I'll go and call your sisters,' I say.

The last time we saw Michael's sisters and their husbands, things were rather strained. It was about two weeks ago, I think. Michael got grumpy with them. It surprised them how changed he was, in stature and temperament. He'd got out of bed and sat up in his leather armchair in the living room. I had to take him to the loo. They went into the garden to make small talk, but I know they could hear our struggles through the open window.

Later, when he was back in bed, they sat and chatted with him like hospital visitors. They wanted to talk about memories and mother and father and roots and childhood things, but he was uncooperative. Nostalgia is a place best visited when there's still plenty of time to enjoy it and to lay down new memories. Otherwise, it is just a reminder of everything that's about to be lost.

Perhaps this was how Michael contained the enormity of what was happening to him. Perhaps his personality changes just made him uncooperative and stubborn. Either way, that's just the way it was.

I find the first number on the redial and picture Sister One in her bedroom or her kitchen or in her living room, drifting through my imagination from one space to the next. The vivid marine blue-green paint of her living room, the tapestry on the wall behind her bed, the little table-for-two in the kitchen. Her voice was a relief to hear.

'But it's so sudden! I knew to expect it, but not now, not yet.' Then a pause where we both speak of loss and regret and sadness and disbelief. 'Now, is there anything I can do, anything at all? I'll let the family know,' she says.

I seem completely incapable of articulating anything meaningful and feel like I'm letting her down.

It's 7.30 am by the time I finish making the calls. I go to Michael and tell him what I've managed so far. I will have to call the surgery and the undertaker and our Mac Nurse, but I can't do that right now. *It's okay, love*, he says, *there's no rush.*

Polly and Sukey come into the room. They meow at me and Michael. I don't want them to jump on him, so I shoo them out into the kitchen and find them some food. They tuck in, simultaneously chewing and purring, oblivious to the new household configuration.

I decide I better phone my neighbours to let them know the news, before they see comings and goings, before I see them in the street, and they ask me how Michael is. Neighbour One is gentle, reassuring, and consoling, offering help that I know will be given but won't be overbearing. Neighbour Two says a simple sorry, and thanks for letting her know. The third is effusively kind but insists on visiting.

'No, no, it's okay. I'm fine. Really.'

'But there must be something I can do.'

I know it's well meant, but I can't cope with talking to anyone, face-to-face. And I imagine someone bustling in and going to gawp at Michael, who is now incapable of fending off prying advances. 'No really, please don't, thanks all the same.'

Five minutes later, there's a knock on the door. I'm still in my pyjamas and dressing gown. I look through the spyhole, and the neighbour is there, standing on the step. Although I don't want to, I'm not strong enough to resist, so I open the door a crack.

'Oh, my poor dear,' she says, putting her hand

to her mouth, and making a sobbing noise that at this moment feels like a bad melodrama version of grief. There are no tears. Nothing about her reaction feels authentic. I feel it's more about her being the first on the scene to offer emergency aid.

We all need to feel useful at times of crisis, but I feel like my loss has been ambushed, before even I have grasped it.

Perhaps she has the best of intentions, but I'm incapable of seeing things other than through the lens of complete abandonment. My defences are high. I have lost my compass and my means of calibration.

'Anything I can do, anything at all, just ask.'

I stumble through 'Yes, well, thanks, but I must go,' holding the door open just a crack, so as not to allow a view past me and into the sacred mausoleum of our home.

'Be strong,' she says, gripping my arm.

Leave me alone! I want to scream, *just leave me alone, all of you!* But I don't. I just close the door, turn my back to it and slide to the floor, where I stay for a while, crumpled like old clothes.

8 am

After an unfelt period has passed, I pick myself up from the floor and go in to see Michael. I tell him about the neighbours and their concerns and kindnesses. I reach under the duvet to find his right hand. It has become cold to the touch, and I recoil at the sensation of it. I lift the cover a little further. I want to see it, but I don't want to see it.

A dark patch is growing from the underside of his arm, where the blood has pooled. I read about this on a cancer care website, in the section about *what to expect when someone dies*. The darkening patches, along with drifting into unconsciousness, were the *signs to look out for* when death was close, but none of these things happened to Michael and I feel cheated out of the proper order of things.

How is it that things moved so quickly before

I realised what was happening? Before I had a chance to alert Will and Alice? Before any of us had a chance to say goodbye?

Michael's face is a waxwork, his large ear lobes are yellowing and have crumpled up. He looks at me through milky glass, from under the half-open slits of his eyelids.

I decide to go upstairs and get into bed, and then bury myself in the duvet, curling into a singularity. It's all gone. Not just Michael, but the future, the things we planned, the life I expected living. Until 6 am, I was part of something much bigger than me. I was a step-mum, a sister-in-law, and part of Michael's extended family. In a rush, it comes to me how fragile all of this was, how dependent it all was on Michael and that without him, I am like Cinderella at midnight. Everything transformed into something smaller, greyer, silent. I know that there is love in my extended family, but I also know that with Michael's death, it has changed forever and that I am basically alone.

9 am

I call the surgery to notify them. The GP will need to come out and issue the death certificate at some point today.

I call Janet, the Mac Nurse. I tell her about how it all ended, and she tells me that Michael loved us all so much that he didn't want to leave. She also promises to call round in a couple of days.

Then I call the undertaker to arrange for Michael to be collected from the house. 'Not until later,' I say. 'I'm not ready for him to go yet.'

In between these calls, I wander around the house. I look in on Michael and update him on my progress. I go back to our, now my, bedroom, walk around the bed, and out again. I clean my teeth. I put the kettle on three times without making a drink. What's the point? I think about the nature of time, and I think about being and not being and how I've entered a liminal space between the two.

10 am

There's absolutely nothing to do.

For the past year, and especially for the last few weeks, my days have been prescribed. My purpose has been to serve, to make better, to make comfortable. I have barely left the house other than to drive to the chemist across town to collect prescriptions or to collect groceries. I've not seen friends or colleagues. The visits from the care team have been welcome, but have left me feeling like a failure.

Perhaps people, family, and medical staff think that Michael and I had a deep conversation about what he wanted for his care as he became more poorly, and about where he wanted to be at the end.

We didn't.

There was no moment of pause to assess my capacity or capability for caregiving or to determine what support we might need. We drifted into this position by default. I have just had to get on with it and do the best I can. Through no fault of their own, the visits from relatives have not brought support or respite. Rather, they have extended my burden of care to them.

I am beyond tired, but I am so programmed to activity in the face of weariness that I can't keep still and don't know what to do with myself. Pacing, sitting, touching things in the house, drying a mug, talking to the cats, waiting, and then the terrible moment of remembering the reality each time I look in on Michael.

11 am

I decide I'd better get dressed, as Mum and Dad will arrive in an hour, or thereabouts. I find jogging bottoms, a T-shirt, and a hoodie.

At 11.15 am, the personal care women call round for their regular session, and I break the news about Michael. They look surprised and say, 'Sorry, dear,' turn and walk away down the path, muttering to each other.

I spend a while reading through the folders that the nurses have left on the table. They contain a daily record of Michael's condition, symptoms and the medications administered. 'Found Michael bright and responsive today.' 'Today Michael was more tired.' 'Wife says Michael has been more confused and seeing things that aren't there.' 'Increased dexamethasone to improve appetite.'

12 pm

Mum and Dad arrive. I open the door to them and Mum steps inside, opens her arms wide, and enfolds me. We move through into the living room. Mum's gaze rests on the dining table with its medicines and sharps box and folders and she exchanges a pained glance with Dad.

'Can I go in and see Michael?' she says. I nod and she leaves me on the sofa, goes into Michael's room and closes the door behind her. She's in there for some time, saying goodbye, maybe expressing her regret. Perhaps thinking about her own mortality, given the metastasised breast cancer she's living with. I can only imagine the impact of this confrontation with death.

She's visibly shaken when she returns. She last saw Michael at Christmas when he still had a full head of hair and looked fairly well. It's not only the reality of the death, but also the evidence of his decline: the hollowed cheeks and wispy hair, giving some inkling of what the last months have been about.

Also, it's the paraphernalia of disease and its wrongness in our house: the hospital bed, the frame around the toilet. She knows how tough I've found things, especially Michael's personality changes, as we've spoken about it most nights, but nothing quite prepared her for the reality.

1 pm

Mum and Dad have gone to the Co-op for some supplies. The fridge is empty apart from the souring end of a carton of milk and the eight remaining ready meals from the last Tesco delivery. I can't bear to have these in the house anymore, so while they're out, I get a rubbish sack, chuck the lot in, and put it outside in the dustbin.

The district nurses call round to collect the controlled medicines and the folders and the sharps box. They count the phials of morphine, checking them off against their records. They put everything in a large, clear plastic box.

At 1.30 pm, the GP calls round to record the death. He spends some time with Michael and writes out a death certificate, which he gives to me, stating the date and time of death, place of death and cause of death: Adenocarcinoma of the Lung.

I tell him about the difficult last hours and with a shrug of his shoulders he says, 'It happens,' adding, 'I'll let the undertakers know they can collect Michael's body when they're ready.'

He's strangely detached, which I find unsettling. My dead husband, the GP's former patient, is unmoving on the bed between us. The most terrible event occurred in this room only a matter of hours before. The course of history has changed and will describe a future in which Michael has no part. It is a deeply serious matter. How can he be so casual about it, so matter of fact?

He has no words of consolation to offer me. There's no tenderness or concern. His task is procedural, and now it's completed. And because I couldn't stop my husband from dying, or by some means of divination know precisely when the event might occur and therefore prepare myself and the family for the moment, and gather all around the bed to stand vigil, I feel that I have failed us all. The GP's shrugged shoulders seem to me to confirm the fact.

His is the sort of 'Oh, well, don't worry about it,' level of response that you might use to lessen the sting if a friend had dropped a slice of toast on the floor butter side down, or bought all the ingredients for a birthday cake but forgotten the eggs. Small, redeemable errors, irksome but of little consequence.

2 pm

Mum makes some lunch of salad leaves, tomato and slices of ham. 'You *must* eat something,' she says.

I've lost a lot of weight and I'm swamped by my jogging bottoms and hoodie. I curl up on the sofa, while Mum and Dad eat at the table.

After lunch I call the register office, where we married seven years ago, to make an appointment for the next day to register Michael's death.

3 pm

When the undertaker comes for Michael, I'm standing in the kitchen with my back to the cupboard by the fridge-freezer. Dad is making tea and Mum is washing up. I let them in, two sombre men in funereal garb carrying a bag.

'Wait a moment,' I say and go in one last time to see Michael.

Despite everything, now it comes down to it I don't want them to take him away. I hold him and kiss his face, his forehead, and his eyes. I hold his icy hand and press my cheek against the slab of his chest.

'I don't want you to go, I don't want you to go, I don't want you to go.' I leave wet traces on his waxy face and damp patches on the duvet. 'Don't go, don't go, wake up, just wake up, please.' I hold him by the shoulders as if to shake him awake, but he is solid, unmoving.

There's a knock on the door. It's time.

'I'm sorry. I love you.' I say to Michael, one last time, and pull myself away to let the tall, strange men into this most intimate of intimate spaces, the place where we shared the last of everything.

'We'll take care of things from here, dear,' the bald one says. Then already they are stripping the bed and tugging the pillow from under Michael's jaw. It's too much to bear and I leave the room, pulling the door shut.

I return to my place in the kitchen and lean with my back against the cupboard from where I can see down the hallway to the door of Michael's room.

Moments later the door opens, and the men are at either end of a long canvas sack of my husband, each grasping a metal loop of a carrying handle that is edged with red plastic.

They bag him heavily down the hall to the front door, bearing the awkward burden between them.

My legs fail me, and I slide to the floor. All of everything, the last year, the last fourteen, all compressed into this one unceremonious departure from the house that together we made into a home.

4 pm

Mum helps me up off the floor and sits with me in the living room. Dad hovers over us, hand over his mouth in bewilderment, not sure what to do with his newly-widowed daughter. I can feel him looking at me, observing me like I'm an exhibit of grief in a museum of curiosities, wanting to make it better, but helpless in the face of such profound distress.

'Mum,' I plead, 'Mum.'

She sends him off to put the kettle on and to do the drying up, something practical and straightforward and homely.

After a while, Mum heads back to the kitchen and busies herself making a meal: chicken casserole, mashed potatoes, and vegetables. Proper food. Wholesome food. I look out of the patio window at the garden, the fence, the half-finished projects, at nothing much at all.

I return to Michael's room. The bed sheet has gone; perhaps it's wrapped around Michael wherever they've taken him. The duvet is on the floor where they discarded it and the pillows are piled up on the bed. I gather these together, take them upstairs and put them in the spare room. I don't want the pillows or covers washed, but I don't want them in my sight, not now. They are both wonderful and hideous things on which my husband laid his head to rest and on which he died, and right now I must defer my judgment on their fate until another day.

5 pm

Mum has made dinner. I have a small portion of everything and eat it all. I have a glass of red wine. Afterwards, Mum sends me off to have a bath and get to bed. 'You're shattered,' she says. 'We can deal with things together tomorrow.'

Upstairs, the bedroom feels wrong. Michael's alarm clock, a crime thriller paperback, and other paraphernalia are still on his bedside table, even though it's been weeks since he slept upstairs. His dressing gown hangs on a hook on the back of the door. My magenta one hangs on the other hook. Traces of him are everywhere. I can smell him. I press my face into his robe and then into the duvet on his side of the bed and inhale.

I undress, put on my towelling bathrobe, go into the bathroom, and set the taps running. The bubble bath froths the stream of hot water into a churn of soothing scent and foam.

Lying in the bath, I become acutely aware of my body as a living body, sensing, sensual, aching, tired, and hungry. I notice the hollows and shadows, the points of hip bones, and the washboard of my ribs under taut skin.

I run my fingers across this landscape with curiosity, as though tracing the surface of a sculpture and wondering about the forces that moulded it into its form.

Then seconds later, the dam of my attention is burst by an overwhelm of grief. Tears come in great, uncontrollable sobs. Hugging my knees to my chest, I rock myself back and forth. The unbearable sadness of it all, my unspent rage, my terrible anger with Michael for all of this, for what he has put me through, for what he's left me with, irreconcilable with the immensity of my love for him that meant to care for him on this journey of journeys, was the greatest, most precious privilege of my life. My deepest regret for the future he's lost, the future we will not share. I've barely cried since the X-ray, not properly. I've held it together, held us together.

When at last the sobs subside, I lay back, close my eyes and allow the hot water to blanket me. In that safe, warm, held space, I am overcome by tiredness and allow myself to drift into sleep.

When I wake up, the water is tepid and the skin on my hands and feet has turned white and wrinkled.

Back in our bedroom, I can hear Mum and Dad moving around downstairs. Polly and Sukey trot upstairs, making chirruping meows as they do.

They jump onto the bed, purring, and nuzzle me, taking it in turns to push a nose and head under my hand to generate a stroke.

I find my baggy sleeping T-shirt, climb into bed and pull the duvet up to my chin. Polly and Sukey find places to curl up and sleep in the zigzags of my body.

I turn out the light and move closer towards Michael's absence to spoon him, reaching an arm around where he should be.

***

Author's Note

I wrote *36 Hours* because it was the book that I needed to read after my husband's death, but couldn't find. I published it hoping that by sharing my experience, patients and carers might feel less alone, and GPs, consultants and others involved in end-of-life care would gain greater insight into what patients and their loved ones are going through, making a positive difference to the way they guide people through the dying process.

36 Hours is an invitation to every reader to find the courage to have more open and honest conversations about death and dying because there's one thing about which we can be completely certain. No one's getting out of here alive.

It is daunting to have 'that' conversation. We worry it might not be the right time, that we might not find the right words or that our attempts will seem clumsy and unkind. But if we knew that by being more open about what's happening, we might help to ease suffering, dialling down some of the fear and anxiety that can surround the end-of-life and improving experiences for the person dying and those who care for them, then perhaps the discomfort of broaching the subject would feel worth it. For those of us who remain, it doesn't mean we will grieve less, but we might heal sooner.

Caring for someone at end-of-life is one of the hardest jobs you might ever have to face but it's also the deepest privilege and one of the greatest gifts you can give another person. For those of you who are, or have been, in that situation, you have my deepest respect.

Fiona Mason
Wivenhoe, October 2022

Acknowledgements

36 Hours has been many years in the making and I've been blessed with some incredible support along the way. My heartfelt thanks and love to my partner, Andy, and to my dear friends and family, for their patience, care, love, understanding and for encouraging me to keep going.

I am grateful to the generous mentors, and readers of various drafts along the way, whose insightful feedback, encouragement and other invaluable support have contributed to the development of this book, with special mentions to Simone Ali, Charlotte Bernays, Helen Chambers, Sarah Clark, Sasha Dugdale, Bobbie Farsides, Sue Finn, Kate Flatt, Chris Gribble, John Mason, Li Mills, Blake Morrison, Julia Payne, Rachel Tarkenter and Jenny Uglow.

For their diligent, timely and generous work on the text, my special thanks to designer Sara Holloway and proof-reader Alex Scott Fairley.

Any errors that might have slipped through the net are, of course, my own responsibility.

Finally, I gratefully acknowledge Arts Council England for a Developing Your Creative Practice award, which supported the creation of this publication.

Some Useful Resources

Learn more about cancer care:

Macmillan Cancer Support
www.macmillan.org.uk

Cancer Research UK
www.cancerresearchuk.org

To help through loss:

Cruse Bereavement Support
www.cruse.org.uk

Hope Again for young people
www.hopeagain.org.uk

Support with mental health:

Mind
www.mind.org.uk

Samaritans
www.samaritans.org

Word After Word

Word After Word Press is a micro-publisher with a special interest in non-fiction including nature and place writing, life writing and memoir. *36 Hours* is our third publication.

Other titles:
The Making of Ynyslas
Wales the Missing Years

www.wordafterword.org.uk